THE BREATH OF LIFE

THE BREATH OF LIFE

OF LIFE

Using the Power of Ki for Maximum Vitality

KŌZŌ NISHINO

KODANSHA INTERNATIONAL
Tokyo • New York • London

Photos on jacket and pages 103–130 by Yoh Kobayashi; all other photos by
Joel Sackett.

Distributed in the United States by Kodansha America, Inc., 114 Fifth
Avenue, New York, N.Y. 10011, and in the United Kingdom and continen-
tal Europe by Kodansha Europe Ltd., 95 Aldwych, London WC2B 4JF.

Published by Kodansha International Ltd., 17-14 Otowa 1-chome, Bunkyo-
ku, Tokyo 112, and Kodansha America, Inc. Originally published in Japan-
ese under the title of *Nishino-ryu ki no gokui*, copyright © 1996 by Kozo
Nishino. English translation copyright © 1997 by Kodansha International
Ltd. All rights reserved. Printed in Japan.
First edition, 1997.

97 98 99   10 9 8 7 6 5 4 3 2 1

ISBN 4-7700-2022-8

Library of Congress Cataloging-in-Publication Data

A catalog record for this book is available from the Library of Congress

CONTENTS

Introduction

Everyone possesses a touch of genius of some kind, but most people go through life without displaying it. That is a pity, because, as it's often said, "We only get to go around once." We have only one life to live.

Who doesn't remember the expectations of youth, that once-in-a-lifetime moment when life blossoms naturally? We remember brimming with exuberance—full of dreams. Everything we saw seemed wonderfully fresh. Our impressions, expectations, and curiosity inspired our next actions. It was a shame to sleep at night, so boundless was our energy by day, and we could hardly wait until tomorrow. Hopes rise and energy flows from the entire organism; the cells function at full capacity, elevating our body to adulthood.

If this condition were to continue, in all probability we would be able to achieve anything we wished—because our vitality would continue to exert its influence. When we acquire a fully matured body, however, our overall life energy begins to decline. We continue to develop by our acquired abilities, but it becomes increasingly difficult to maintain a youthful outlook directed at the future and continually reinvent ourselves from fresh experiences.

Our unique inherent abilities remain hidden in the shadows. As we grow older, our natural tendency is to become conservative in outlook, take fewer risks, and hold back our enthusiasm. In the East, it is often said that after the age of fifty, special intuitive powers come to the fore. This is considered an accumulation of wisdom, experience, and sophisticated creativity. But I believe this is only possible if the physical body is in optimum condition. With the exception of a small minority of gifted people, most of us, unfortunately, do not reveal new potential when we are well into adulthood.

On the other hand, why is it that celebrated people of ability and position, as they grow older, in most cases seem to be remnants left over from an earlier world in spite of attempts to regain their old enthusiasm . . . as if their bodies lacked vitality? Isn't there some way to hold onto this illusive effervescence, this tenacity, even as we age?

There is a way, but it is not through any conventional means with which we are familiar. It does not have anything to do with thinking. In fact, if there were a single factor that puts a check on our natural birth right to vitality, it would have to be our minds.

"Know the foolishness of adhering to a fixed view of life; live life as a free spirit as befits a human being."

This saying has been repeated down through the ages.

Close to four centuries ago Galileo deduced that the earth turned on its axis, and the authorities of his time—the Church, the emperor, statesmen—tried to discredit his views. Galileo was taken to court and narrowly escaped disaster. Although he acquiesced, his later publications show that he steadfastly stuck to his theory. Giordano Bruno held that the universe had countless suns and that humans and the cosmos shared the same material basis. He was burned as a heretic.

We, in general, fail to be aware of our ignorance and tend to judge matters according to preconceived ideas. We know a limited number of things and no more. Even during Galileo's time it should have been possible through scientific investigation—free of bias—to ascertain that the earth was moving. The problem, as Galileo noted, was not insufficient knowledge, but human weakness, and in particular, weakness in the face of authority.

Unless we rid ourselves of weakness, meaning mental and psychological weaknesses, we are not operating at our full potential.

We think that cerebral activity is what controls individual lives and brings fruitful results or failure. And the strength to overcome weakness, too, is regarded as the realm of mental powers alone.

But there is a fallacy in such a line of thinking. Ever since Descartes' "I think, therefore I am," the mind and spirit have been divorced from the physical body and the former has been accorded too much importance.

Certainly, people must use their intellectual abilities to achieve life goals. But I do not believe the intellect to be the decisive factor in one's "success." Those who succeed in life look back on their past and thank fate (or God, if they clothe it in a divine form). Fortune blooms in the light of life energy.

If we have more life energy, then we become strong and full of vitality, and our luck changes. Strength, which is the freedom to be ourselves, invites providence, and vitality gives us youthfulness. Life energy circulating in the body is a physical condition that acts beneficially on our mind. Is there a method, then, you may ask, to foster this life energy?

The answer is a resounding yes and I honestly feel that I've developed one of the best methods to do so. It is mastering ki—what we call this primal life energy—through the Nishino Breathing Method. This breathing method is a distinctive concept based on my studies in medicine and training in classical ballet and the martial arts. But you don't have to know anything about these fields to be able to do it.

Those who practice these breathing techniques become bright and cheerful. Their cellular functions improve, and their lives change. As they become conscious of their life energy and begin to control it, their lives naturally open up and broaden.

When my first book on the Nishino Breathing Method was released in Japan, I had already confronted many facets of ki, including its influence on the human body and human destiny.

That was in 1987 and ki was quite topical, featured on television and in magazines. It was controversial that during lessons at the Nishino school, students would jump about or "fly," and generally behave in an uncontrollable, chaotic manner. Outsiders, being skeptical about such things, found it hard to believe such reactions could occur after receiving an input of ki energy. The fact that ki itself was not visible to the naked eye challenged common sense.

That ki exists, however, has been confirmed by scientists researching on the cutting-edge. Yet, modern science has provided us with very little enlightenment about it. What I and many others know about it is that in terms of developing potential abilities, recovering from stress and maximizing vitality, ki has had remarkable effects.

My breathing method acknowledges the link between DNA molecules (deoxyribonucleic acid) and ki; it promotes the functions of DNA and the immune system.

What drives the brain is also DNA; if its functions improve, the brain's functions will improve as well. DNA's functions are the power source of life and the brain functions by drawing on that power.

Unlike our psychological and intellectual faculties, which waver constantly, DNA, as the controller of living information, does not change. If the functions of DNA are stable, the efficacy of life energy flows well; that is, the biochemical activities of our cells operate at an optimum level, allowing us to fully imbibe the experience of life.

Back in August 1994 I had the pleasure of giving a special lecture to over 1,000 doctors and other health professionals from around the world in Tokyo at the Fourth International Congress on Traditional Asian Medicine. In September of that year I also was invited to give a lecture before national and private university physical education professors sponsored by the All Japan Collegiate Athletic Association. It was an opportunity for me to offer a different perspective on "physical education."

I was fortunate in that the Nishino Breathing Method was welcomed by both the medical world and by university physical education professors; that is, by two groups of experts on the human body. When my book was first published, there was much speculation and discussion about my breathing method. But finally, it seems, my method has become accepted by the "establishment."

Nowadays the term "cellular intelligence" is commonly used to refer to the complex functions that our cells fulfill in sustaining life. How this intelligence is affected by ki is a topic of increasing interest to molecular biologists and other scientists. I couldn't be more pleased about this direction, because I recognize that much of our expectations and beliefs are molded a great deal by scientific validation. Hopefully, the Nishino Breathing Method can make a contribution to current research. At the same time, however, it is my firm belief that what will ultimately advance our societies toward a more peaceful and prosperous world is the shifting of our cerebral intelligence-centered paradigm to a new one based on cellular intelligence. Which is why, as a tiny step toward this goal, I'm taking this opportunity to introduce my life philosophy and breathing techniques to a foreign audience for the first time. The Nishino Breathing Method triumphs over our human weaknesses, nourishing ki through a technique that anyone can master.

For over a decade now, I have had thousands of students attend my two schools in Tokyo and Osaka, and each day I exchange ki energy with several hundred of them. I can say that no matter how much I may think I know about ki, practically everyday brings marvelous new discoveries.

Whatever your circumstances may be, ki is the life support. I have no doubt that my method will carry over cultural, religious, or philosophical boundaries, cultivating the "intelligent body" that will fortify you to cope with life's complexities and enable you to experience its joys in ways never before possible. The method's effectiveness will depend on the individual, but I can assure you that if you practice it regularly, you will reap its benefits.

CHAPTER 1

The Wonders of Innate Power

All the Body's Cells Have an Intelligence

What is innate power? Since it is a term that I often use, let's start by examining this power's biological origin.

The human body is an organism composed of some 60 trillion cells.

Each of these cells are home to chromosomes, which, in turn, are composed of 3 billion sequentially ordered base pairs of molecules (adenine, guanine, thymine, and cytosine in certain combinations). These bases, so called because they form the rungs of the ladder of the DNA structures, are the units which make up genes. Each gene is one sequence of bases along the double helix of DNA and can be anywhere from a few dozen to a few thousand base pairs. There are about 100,000 genes in humans, encoded with information that enables them to make many different kinds of protein molecules. Protein molecules, or enzymes, as we know most of them, are the workhorses of each cell in your body; they "run" the chemical reactions in your cells. The volume of information contained in these genes, as you might imagine, is an unspecified quantity. The information comprises the cell's contribution—along with the 60 trillion other cells in the human body—to providing the chemical functions, including cell reproduction, to sustain life.

Our cells are specialized and share the work of keeping our machinery running. They are organized into organs and other components, which make up subsystems of our body. This combination of systems makes us what we are—a complex, complete organism.

Each of our cells, thus, contributes to the whole effort. We might posit that each cell, therefore, is an intelligent entity, one of a huge family which makes possible our physical abilities.

Next, the same genetic data will increase in surprising quantity depending on the environment, another important basis for making possible the release of innate power. Consider, for example, that a common tomato plant can produce 10,000 or more tomatoes. Such a quantity is due not to bioengineering but to providing these plants with the ideal environment, where hydroponic cultivation adjusts for nutrition, sunlight, gas, and temperature.

Environmental influence is not limited to plants alone, of course. In India in 1920, a feral virgin named Kamala was discovered who had been brought up by wolves until the age of about eight. She was taken into human society but would not behave like a human being despite efforts to train her. She crawled about, eating without using her hands, and even ran on all fours faster than when erect. Efforts to teach her to speak only enabled her to use fragmented speech. This example shows the impediments an environment can produce.

Aquatic creatures, too, show us the influence of their habitat. Chimanta, a remarkable geographical feature 2200 meters high in Venezuela, underwent a great change 1.7 billion years ago when the earth's crust dramatically altered, the sides of the mountain sinking over 2,000 meters (6,560 ft) into the earth and leaving part of Chimanta as a mesa. This table-like formation rises above its surroundings. In recent years a group of explorers entered Chimanta's mysterious sanctum to do zoological research and discovered that the ecosystem of the higher reaches was entirely different from that of at sea level because of the great altitude gap of more than 1000 meters (3,280 ft) between them.

For example, at 10,000-meter (32,800 ft) elevations, catfish attained only a few centimeters in length, while in rivers at lower elevations the same species 80-cm (32 in) could be seen. Changes in the earth's surface had divided the ecosystem at different elevations, producing curious results in biological life.

In 1909, Austrian biologist Paul Kammerer (1880–1926) conducted an experiment using the reproductive traits of the salamander. Leaving aside his claim that acquired traits can be inherited, which was much criticized, our interest here is in how life forms have the ability to adapt to the environment. In one of several controversial experiments, he took the viviparous (live-bearing) Alpine salamander and showed how it could acquire certain characteristics of the spotted oviparous (egg-laying) lowland salamander and vice versa. When the Alpine salamander was put in an artificial lowland environment, its offspring, normally born two at a time on land, were now born in water—as tadpoles. On the other hand, the lowland salamander, when put in an artificially-produced highland environment, after several aborted attempts in producing tadpoles where no waters existed, succeeded in giving birth to two offspring.

Clearly, the environment exerts a great influence on living creatures. I believe these changes play a decisive role in the extent to which innate power is manifested, whether animal, plant, or human. Through the Nishino Breathing Method (NBM) you can create a body that will set the course of your potential abilities in the right direction.

The creation of an ideal body with the NBM requires application of a concept called *chūyū*, most easily implemented by effective breathing. Chūyū is a condition that can be compared to the pleasant feelings of being in a hot springs bath and letting the body float gently.

宙遊

chū yū

"playing in the universe"

| Relaxing Provides the Spark

It is that utterly relaxed state of being that is often conducive to inspiring, for example, creative works, scientific discoveries, insights, inventions, and so on. The discovery by Archimedes of the principle of buoyancy while in his bath is well known. I have no doubt that while Archimedes was in his bath his body was in a state of chūyū. Many others, too, hit upon brilliant ideas while they were in the bath. Taikan Yokoyama, a celebrated Japanese sumie-ink painter, never failed to bathe every morning before taking up his brush.

There are many, also, who have had a burst of inspiration while taking a walk. Ancient Greece had a group within Aristotles' clique, the peripatetics, who probably knew that they were at their cerebral best when out together for a stroll. German philosopher Immanuel Kant was devoted to strolls, going out for a walk every day at the same hour. Nikola Tesla, of whom it is said that he invented the twentieth century together with Thomas Edison, was taking a walk one evening with his friend through a city park in Budapest when he began reciting a verse from a poem he'd memorized, then suddenly stopped.

He picked up a small twig and drew a small picture in the sand. The picture was the induction motor in its entirety. Seven years later the design he submitted to the American Institute of Electrical Engineers was identical to the picture he drew in the sand that fateful night.

Lying in bed at night is another example of bringing on the chūyū state of being. Hideki Yukawa, it is said, received the clue to his Nobel Prize-winning meson theory (accounting for the force binding protons and neutrons in atomic nuclei) while snug in bed. Another Nobel laureate, the scientist Kenichi Fukui, unfailingly placed a pencil and paper near his pillow before turning in. Kiyoshi Oka, a respected Japanese mathematician, makes certain mathematical observations while having his ears cleaned in the barber shop and says he then hits upon the mathematical proof behind them in a matter of minutes. Most likely, while having his ears cleaned he probably forgets himself and assumes a transcendent chūyū state of being.

When painting La Gioconda ("Mona Lisa"), Da Vinci tried a number of ploys to lift the mood of his model and thus evoke from her a soft, lovely expression. He had a group play music and sing songs, and even hired a clown. Da Vinci put her in a chūyū condition and then set about painting the mysterious smile of the woman that sat before him.

Chūyū can bring inspiration to the minds of scientists and mathematicians, elevate the sensitivity of artists, and elicit beautiful, enigmatic facial expressions.

What other methods have been available to us in the past to bring about such uncommon experiences? Sages have sat upright for prolonged periods, immersed in the forest, trying to be in tune with the surrounding world. They could regale themselves with their accumulated ascetic skills and assume a body free and at one with nature. In this way, they invited enlightenment.

Astronauts returning to earth on the Apollo 15 said that in space they had several times the capabilities they had on earth. During operations on the lunar surface they knew simply by looking at a partner's face what that partner would do. Intuitive knowledge blossomed, they have said, adding that they had special mental faculties while on the moon.

Former astronaut James Irwin speculated that the reason for this phenomenon was that because of their specially designed spacecraft and spacesuits they were able to breathe more efficiently and thus achieve greater abilities than when on earth.

While there may be a variety of means to reach the chūyū state, I think the quickest and most efficient way is through the NBM. Adding my breathing exercises to your daily routine will enable you to achieve a body capable of such abilities that I mentioned right here on earth. Once you've acquired ideal breathing skills and a "free-floating" chūyū body, latent powers reveal themselves as you need them—in everyday life, sports, and all manner of other activities.

How is breathing in the chūyū state different from controlled, forceful breathing exercises? Consider aerobics, an activity that utilizes oxygen to produce energy. When done properly, aerobic exercises increases our capacity to take in oxygen and transport the oxygen to the heart, lungs, muscles, circulatory systems and other necessary areas of the body to produce energy to do work.

The relaxed chūyū state creates a powerful body based on proper breathing.

The point I want to make here is that contrary to the "no pain, no gain" fitness fanaticism prevalent during the 70s and 80s, and according to a U.S. Presidential committee report on health and sports some years ago, recent research indicates that sports activities involving little stress and coercion—i.e., aerobics-like activities having a low level of heartbeats as their objective—are better for the health. In fact, Kenneth Cooper, the father of aerobics and founder of the Cooper Aerobics Center in Dallas, who believed at one time too that "the more you exert yourself, the better" gradually came around to a more prudent way of thinking.

The chūyū state places no great burden on either the heart or the lungs; it creates a relaxed yet powerful body based on proper breathing.

Loosen and Twist to Create the Ideal Body

As the means to achieve chūyū, the ideal physical condition, I have devised a program of exercises for loosening up ("kanyō") and twisting ("sennen") the body in various specific ways (see Chapter 5, especially "karin").

Loosening the body means to relieve it of its application of force and tension and to relax completely, while retaining only the control required to do the exercise properly. Simply to twist suggests applying strength to the shoulders and arm muscles, firming the hips and twisting almost as if squeezing. Not so. The entire body must be loosened and one must twist smoothly and naturally. Chūyū, thus, is the physical condition created by the mutual interaction of loosening and twisting.

To clearly symbolize the meanings of loosening and twisting as I perceive them, I created these special terms "kanyō" and "sennen." When certain people attempt to do the preliminary exercise "karin," I notice that if I merely

Chūyū is created by the mutual interaction of loosening and twisting.

tell them to loosen up and twist they've grasped only the superficial meaning of the words but are not comprehending with their bodies at all. To overcome this problem, I coined the words "kanyō" and "sennen."

緩揺
kan yō

The two characters for "kanyō" are "kan" and "yō." Notice that kan has two multistroke parts: a radical on the left that means thread or string and a larger part to its right that means relax. Kan means metaphorically "to loosen the thread" or to give latitude. "Yō" expresses the idea of a cradle being rocked so that for a while it continues to sway.

"Kanyō," then, suggests loosening up the body in the sense of the imagery implicit in the character. A few English words having related meanings that come to mind are "flow," "modulate," "sway," and "swing."

The two characters for "sennen" are "sen" and "nen." 旋捻
"Sen," too, has a radical on the left and a multistroke unit   sen nen
to the right of it. The radical means "square." Together
they suggest a regulated and repeated movement around
the square and a return to the starting point. The analogy
with a twisting type of exercise is clear.

"Nen" follows the same structural pattern of the others: radical on the left, descriptive multistroke unit on the
right. It suggests words such as "intertwine," "wrap around,"
"twist," and "to have tenacity and perseverance." Compa-
rable meanings may be seen in the English words "turn,"
and "spiral."

These two qualities of chūyū, which will become clear-
er as you read on, are a part of all my breathing exercises
in Chapter 5.

The Body Seeks
Unlimited Freedom

Humans are bound spatially and temporally; that is,
they are restricted by their bodies and by time. Like it or
not, we experience these confines everyday. If we don't
clear up one thing at a time, nothing gets done, and an
individual's sphere of action, no matter how hard one
tries, is limited.

At the same time, however, we also embrace lives
which go beyond our individual existences. The reason
we can feel with our bodies when we hear great music is
because in such moments worlds beyond ourselves open
up. The fact that when we stand before the works of such
master painters as Matisse and Picasso, we are enraptured
by them, owes itself to the universality of the human body.

Equally, when we are engrossed in a task and hit upon a brilliant idea, there is the sense of a link between the self and unlimited existence.

Such a body is reaching out for a link with the cosmos. This quality, too, is a part of the condition referred to in the NBM as chūyū, wherein innate power is most likely to manifest. And the twisting and loosening of the body—kanyō and sennen—lead to it.

Let's explore this idea of the link with the cosmos a little more.

If we allow our bodies to be guided in an ideal direction, it will seek harmony with the universe, and expand and develop as a result. An exceptional dancer will move with such elegance as to seem to embody the universe. In the same manner, a good athlete's movements are able to draw in spectators completely.

One opportunity for the body to acquire freedom of movement is to feel the air passing as a medium between humans and the outside world. Usually, of course, people don't feel the existence of air. But air itself is what gives people life. An astronaut who had returned from space once said, "People live in atmosphere," a fact he had not felt as keenly before.

Water is a more resilient medium than air. If we observe the way fish swim without going against the current, we can understand exactly how they are at one with the water. In the same way, birds fly as gracefully as they do because they instinctively adopt the air as their medium. I believe that humans, too, if they can sense the air by breathing deeply, can make it possible for the body to expand beyond its physical boundaries.

When I was studying at the Metropolitan Opera Ballet

School in New York in the 50s, the internationally renowned ballet choreographer Antony Tudor taught that "when you extend your hand, do it with the feeling that you want to reach the wall." I think he meant feeling the air between the wall and the hand and acquiring the sensation that it is extending as far as the wall. Marvellous dancers perform while radiating vibrations as if confirming the tactile nature of the air. This is the kind of link with the cosmos that frees the body.

"Fluctuation" Affords Compatibility with the Environment

Chūyū has much in common with the concept of "fluctuation" referred to in physics, statistics, and biology. It conveys meanings such as "wavering," "ebb and flow," "undulation," "vibration," and "changeableness."

For example, the volume of matter in thermodynamics is expressed as average molecular weight, and the variations around that average are called fluctuations. This fluctuation is calculated mathematically. More generally, concerning living and non-living things and events of all kinds, the range of movement of a thing is its fluctuation.

Somewhere between these random and systematic fluctuations are those that are manifested by living organisms—which combine the two in a flexible and stable form. It is this type of fluctuation that produces the maximum levels of human ability.

When we look at something, for example, the eye constantly moves, and particularly so in those instances when the object being viewed is motionless. If we do not move our eyeballs, or even if they move but the image received by the retina is kept from moving, before long the eyes will stop seeing. Of course if the eyeballs move too much, objects will become indistinguishable. The human being's visual acuity is possible through the tiny fluctuations of the eyeballs.

The colors of famous paintings, the fluctuations of lines, the fluctuations of sonorities in famous musical compositions—all these, if examined, would agree in nature with the fluctuations of living organisms.

Again, for the very reason that genetic characteristics of living things pass from parent to child and from child to grandchild with slight "fluctuations" creates the adaptability required to survive in the changing environment. Variation ensures the efficient functioning of organic systems so that they continue to evolve. The NBM activates the chūyū state, producing the "fluctuation" important to developing individual potential abilities.

Open-and-Close, a Natural Law

Another important element that connects breathing and chūyū is the NBM's law of open-and-close. "Open" refers to opening up the body, or, concretely, to bring together the shoulder blades, stimulating the chest muscles; in the final analysis it means liberating the functions of the brain. At this time it is important to expel the breath. If you open up your body as you deeply, softly expel your breath, your body relaxes and drifts off endlessly into the universe, completely emancipated. The body and the universe become as one, borders vanish, and a deliciously free, refreshed mood takes over. When the body is open you feel that you're communicating through it with the universe.

"Closed" means the body is closed, where the chest is contracted. One's breathing becomes thin and long. At this time the body is storing energy. Energy is taken in naturally by the in-breath, and when closed, the body can be fully responsive to the self.

Following this law of open-and-close, you can, while taking smooth, deep breaths, rapidly achieve chūyū.

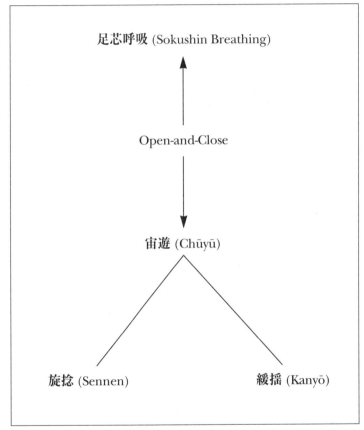

Attaining chūyū through the open-and-close law.

Observing animals is a good way to understand just how the law of open-and-close conforms to nature's principles. When animals poise to pounce upon their quarry, they tense up their bodies—close them—and breathe in, and in the next moment they attack their prey while releasing their energy and opening up their bodies. The NBM is so devised as to carry out different patterns of breathing in conformance with the law of open-and-close, which you will actually experience when you practice the breathing exercises.

In the NBM, your body relaxes and "opens" to the universe as the breath is expelled.

Once you start using the NBM, your entire body begins to firm up and slim down so that people notice a change in you. Since oxygen is delivered throughout your body, your internal organs perk up and function well and very quickly the body is refreshed. Next, a strange sort of energy flows outward from within the body. That's not all. When the body fills up with vitality, the five senses—sight, hearing, smell, taste, and touch are sharpened—as well as your intuitive sense.

Also, your abilities to comprehend things and to assimilate improve markedly. You naturally develop an eagerness for everything, working briskly and finding yourself producing the best results. You of course acquire greater confidence in yourself.

If you achieve fundamental change from deep within your physical body with the NBM, this latent power steadily flows outward and you can achieve a favorable life cycle—one that brings on one good thing after another.

Let me cite a few examples of how practicing the NBM enabled people to draw out their potential. These students shared with me their remarkable experiences, thanking me for introducing them to better breathing. A student in the science and engineering department of a famous private university in central Tokyo made up his mind to take the medical school examination for the first time. A trial examination yielded a disappointing evaluation: "Qualification for entrance unfeasible; change choice of schools."

Since he had attended an affiliated high school, he had taken the "examinationless escalator" to enter his current university. Results of his trial examination showed that his academic level in test points placed him in the first year of high school. After a year of practicing the NBM four times a week, in less than half a year of examination study he qualified for three medical schools.

A number of golfers who began using the NBM improved their golf abilities enough to win tournaments. Golf is a sport with a particularly strong mental aspect and by using this breathing method and thus centering one's feeling, the result is a suddenly higher score. "The ball didn't rise" and "I just tapped the ball and it traveled much farther than before" are commonly heard comments from players. As well, the ability to concentrate naturally increases and game-winning putts tend to be more frequent.

An international medical equipment manufacturer's Japanese company president won eight big competitions in rapid succession. "I'm having trouble finding room for my trophies!" he exclaimed.

The vice president of an international high-tech corporation is also well known for his tennis prowess. He played with Jimmy Connors and with others among the world's ranking professionals. After he began using the NBM he developed a serve and receiving abilities that surprised even the tennis professionals. He was once jokingly asked by a world-class circuit player, "Let's team up for doubles and make a little money"—so much had my student improved in his game.

**An Unrestricted Body
Invites Miracles**

I can cite other examples. A 71-year-old public accountant, very talented and accomplished at writing and composing haiku poems, regularly visits the Osaka branch of the Nishino School. One day, after five months of practicing the NBM, he was told by his mentor of 20 years—an eminent calligrapher and one known for being a severe critic—"What free-flowing, carefree calligraphy you've been writing!" The accountant, himself, was surprised by his own progress.

Although he was over 71 years old, his physique appeared youthfully "reproportioned" by the NBM. His weight had not changed, but his chest fleshed out and his stomach flattened. Since breathing circulates oxygen throughout the body, posture had naturally improved and he gave the impression of vitality and self-possession.

In another case, a man in his forties was also learning the NBM at the Osaka school. As a university student he had been a gymnast. Delighting in his physical agility, he had become a mountaineering guide, climbing the Himalayas, Andes, and other challenging peaks around the world as well as a paraglider. In the winter he is a rock-climbing specialist. He also lectures for the Mountaineering Training Department of the Ministry of Education. In his work as a guide he must lead mountain climbers and assist those in distress.

At the point when he had been studying the NBM for four months, one of his colleagues in the Mountaineering Training Department, a physical training specialist, said to him, "What happened? Your body looks different— really trim."

For quite some time he had been training with exercise machines and had developed a chiseled, muscular body, to supplement his technique in gymnastic movements. At the same time, though, he'd become muscle-bound. He commented, "I got acquainted with the NBM and for the first time I really discovered how free and loosened up my body could feel."

One day he took off for a test flight on a paraglider and at a height of about 15 meters (49 ft) it was caught in a sudden wind. One of its wings broke and it fell in a spiraling motion, tailspinning down and crashing to earth. It was a question of whether he'd suffer sudden death—or break every bone in his body.

In the moment he sensed danger the NBM's chūyū principle flashed across his mind and—miraculously—his body relaxed. Had he been able to apply the level of technique he'd acquired through gymnastics he'd have probably been able to more or less withstand injuries sustained on impact, but at such a height and speed, that was not possible.

He slammed into the earth with a somersault and was thrown several yards. For good measure, his forehead hit a rock. Later, with a large bandage applied to his head, he attended his next breathing practice session and drew applause with his account of what had happened. In any case, he saved his own life. No—I should say that his life was saved by his latent power.

Breathing Enhances Natural Healing Power

So what changes are apparent with the NBM? First of all, it builds a healthy, resilient body. The method also has a great beneficial effect on those who have lost their health. I was once thanked by a young woman afflicted with nephrotic syndrome (kidney malfunction) who was able, through the NBM, to regain her health and bear a child. There are others who have been able to cure themselves of uterine tumors. It also appears that the NBM proves marvelously effective in certain chronic illnesses offering no hope of recovery. Stiff shoulders, back pain, cold extremities, and so forth are done away with. Many students say they have recovered from nearsightedness and farsightedness.

The word illness in Japanese (*byō-ki*) literally means an illness associated with breathing (*ki*). Japanese know the meaning of the word but use it unconsciously and out of habit, so perhaps few recognize the close relationship between illness and respiration. Many illnesses can be prevented by changing the manner of one's breathing.

病気
byō ki

For example, cancer occurs when cells undergo a mutation. During one's sixties there is a greater tendency to develop cancer cells. Whether or not cancer cells develop depends on how smoothly one's circulatory system functions. With effective oxygen utilization each cell is vitalized, cancerous cells are trapped. I think this theory stands to reason.

As an illustration of the efficacy of oxygen, I relate an interesting story I heard. The owner of a famous blowfish restaurant in Osaka that I sometimes go to recalled the following incident:

"I've nearly died trying to get the fullest enjoyment from eating blowfish. I once ate the liver, the most dangerous part, and suddenly my body became numb, and before I knew it I was on my way to the hospital in an ambulance. My condition was so serious that there seemed to be little chance of revival. They flushed out my stomach and put me on an oxygenator. I miraculously survived—according to the doctor."

There are different aspects of oxygen; while free radicals exert a harmful effect upon living organisms, normal oxygen can be beneficial. The blowfish restaurant owner's account is an amazing example of the importance of effective oxygen delivery in the human body. In any case, it's helpful to recognize the links between illness and breathing on the one hand and the body and breathing on the other.

That said, the NBM was not conceived as a cure for illness nor as a way of prevention. Rather, from its inception, its aim has been to manifest potential abilities and promote an assertive way of living life—a method that maximizes the experience of life itself.

As Buddha said, so long as one is living it is impossible never to become ill. However, when you practice my breathing method, oxygen circulates well throughout the body and natural healing power increases. At the point when treatment becomes necessary, experience has shown that the body will suddenly exhibit the beneficial effects of treatment. A body that fails to respond, no matter how much treatment it receives, is lacking in proper energy functions; to create a body replete with efficient energy that recovers quickly when properly treated is of paramount importance.

Hippocrates, the father of medicine, said that the foundation of medicine lies in bringing out the body's natural healing power. The same way of thinking is seen running consistently through the "Medical Standard," long the medical text used in Europe. Modern-day medicine progresses remarkably day by day and gives us amazing results. Even today, though, the effectiveness of modern medicine depends on its ability to draw out natural healing power. The NBM is credited with being effective against disease because it increases one's life energy and natural healing power.

A Changed Body Alters One's Destiny

Many of my students have commented, "Since I began using the NBM my relationships with other people have become smoother," "Business discussions come together the way I want them to," "I was able to get capital from an uncooperative bank," or "My luck is starting to turn." Since breathing is the circulatory system of the universe (the exterior) and the self (the interior), it extends and liberates people.

People who have their backs to the wall often grumble, "Things just aren't going well" and "Everything just turns out wrong even if the intentions behind it are good." Having your back to the wall means losing your link with what's around you, and becoming isolated. The more you try to get out from under, the harder life gets and you become even farther removed from everything around you. Mulling over matters is also no good.

To think things over is of course important, but obsessive thinking obstructs clear-headed results. To give it a physically based explanation, in such a deep-thought mode the shoulders are breathing frantically—that is, you take very quick, shallow breaths—or not at all. By breathing deeply, you are able to naturally connect again with your surroundings—to "compose" your energy and restore the body to normal.

A baseball pitcher who throws a series of poor balls

may prompt his manager to go to the pitcher's mound and have a few casual words with him. Taking this pause permits the pitcher's breathing to be regulated and stabilized.

間合
ma ai

In the world of theater, for example, such a pause on one level refers to reassessing the space, both physical and psychological, for the self vis-a-vis the audience. On another level, it means taking "time out" for oneself and having a breathing pause so that the physical body can be brought up to a more efficient energy level. Called "ma'ai" in Japanese, these three aspects of the "pause" have an important role in Būdō, or the martial arts, and the traditional Japanese arts.

During times of adversity, one's external world seems cold and unresponsive. When we want our surroundings to change, to be receptive to us, then first of all we ourselves must change. Only then will our environment begin to change of its own accord. "God helps those who help themselves," the saying goes. One shouldn't brood and fret but change at the physical level, that is, at the breathing level.

After beginning the NBM, experiencing a turn in good fortune, say, can be an opportunity to put this line of thinking into good use. Even if we were to be confronted by disbelief or misunderstanding ("Don't be silly! Destiny is decided by God!"), we can stand steadfastly, heeding the wonders of the breath, knowing that—"if the physical body changes, one's destiny may also change."

2

Why Pursue
Ki Now?

To some extent, great or small, we all live according to a framework of preconceived notions. But from time to time we encounter events impossible to incorporate into our framework. We attempt to come up with rational theories, based on analysis and observation, and thus broaden our sphere of knowledge.

Particularly with regard to the human body, no matter how we may try to understand it scientifically, it exhibits phenomena beyond our comprehension. Our knowledge is only the tip of the iceberg. The same holds true of "ki," the great primal energy that we are born with and which is all around us. It is an innate, fundamental energy that gives us life, yet, most of us understand actually very little about it.

The knowledge that we have at our disposal cannot yet determine the issues of life, death, and destiny. What controls these issues is dynamic, vital ki, the energy that is the primary component of all physiological, biological activities. How we access this energy and how we apply it has been a theme of never-ending fascination to me.

Until the seventeenth century the motivational power of human life was believed to reside in the heart. Then it was later believed to reside in the brain. It was considered that understanding the brain, from which our ideas and concepts derive, would lead to mastering most of life's mysteries. The brain was thought to be the black box and the key to human civilization in the 21st century.

But in fact, scientific research has shown us that the fountainhead of human life is DNA, that long strand of molecule carrying 3 billion encoded bits of information, including controls for regulating the immune system. I believe future research will focus on studying how to enhance DNA functions, including those of the immune system, with ki—the energy of life.

Since as far back as I can recall, I have walked a path in search of this "biospark"—the vitality of living organisms. Let me share a little bit of my background so you might appreciate how I came to the NBM.

I began the study of medicine at Osaka City University Faculty of Medicine. In medical school my studies of the functions of respiratory and circulatory organs, human anatomy, and sports physiology, the basic structure of the human body, later proved very valuable to me throughout my life. As a medical student at that time I frequented the hospital and thus routinely came face to face with the wonders of human life. I was fascinated by the fact that patients in similar conditions varied greatly in their response to the care give by the same doctors: some patients would die while others recovered. There was some critical factor in determining survival—what was it?

My professor said the reason was differences in their individual life force. Then I began to puzzle over exactly what its properties might be. While it seems now that the election to study medicine was directly related to my pursuit to learn the true "source of life," at the time I intended to become a doctor, and wanted to study the design and structure of the human body from a scientific standpoint.

While in medical school, I came across a book that had a profound effect on me. The book was about Sergei Diaghilev, the Russian impresario and producer who exerted a great influence on the various artistic genres of his time in Europe. Participating in his creative ventures seemed to have drawn out the undiscovered talents of many, and enabled them to forge ahead rapidly. Under his tutelage many first-rate artists developed one after another: composers Stravinsky, Ravel, Glazunov, Prokofiev, Debussy; artists Bakst, Benov, Picasso, Matisse; writers Claudel, Cocteau; choreographers Massine, Balanchine; dancers Pavlova, Nijinsky, Karsavina, Mordkin, Cecchetti, Markova, Lifar, and others.

With youthful enthusiasm building up inside me, I took this book in hand, threw away everything expected of me as a future doctor, and instead chose ballet. Just about that time, Ichizo Kobayashi, owner of Hankyu Railways Group and founder of the Takarazuka Musical Dance Revue, planned to establish in Japan a true Western-style ballet company, and for the first time in its history the women-only world that was Takarazuka boldly opened its portals to male dance students. Conditions for entry were that aspirants be attending university or already about to graduate and in good health and keen on becoming dancers.

Some 700 aspirants all over Japan responded to this call. Only three were accepted. Half a year later I alone was sent to Tokyo to study ballet. A year later, by an unorthodox selection procedure, I became a Takarazuka Music School ballet instructor and choreographer. The other two accepted into the program, together with five who joined later, became my students. My first pupil at Takarazuka was Ineko Arima, who later became a popular actress for the Toho Movie Company.

Later, in 1951, I entered the Metropolitan Opera Ballet School in New York as a foreign student to learn ballet in its authentic form. Thus I became the first Japanese ever to enroll in the school in the highest-level class geared for professional dancers. From Antony Tudor and from Margaret Craske, a disciple of Cecchetti (who had instructed ballet dancers such as Nijinsky and Pavlova), I studied the very soul of ballet.

In 1953 I returned to Japan and founded the Nishino Ballet Troupe in Osaka. And, amazingly, in the following year my troupe had matured enough to stage "Giselle" in its entirety.

Front-Rank Artists Induce Vibrations

As sentient beings, we have the ability to move and be moved. This was most apparent to me in the world of the theater, where a particular vitality seemed to make the difference in a performance. Could it be that this vitality—or life energy—was related to our senses? I began to see that all five senses—and the sixth sense as well—have a basis in life energy and that when the senses are fully engaged, an extraordinary performance is possible.

As you may be aware, ballet training methods have advanced in step with progress in knowledge of anatomy. Their relationship is particularly pronounced in regard to joint and muscle functions. In world-renowned institutions such as the School of American Ballet and the Paris Opera Ballet School, dancers with artistic promise and ideal physical proportions study by using the body's physiology and traditional ballet training principles to reach the highest level of dance technique.

Even assuming an ideal aptitude and physique for ballet, after more than ten years of training, very few dancers become topflight performers. To satisfy the viewing audience requires something beyond appearance and technique—charisma and that "undefinable something"—that quality beyond the ordinary. The rare ballet dancers, opera singers, conductors and other performers enthrall viewers the moment they appear on stage.

My intuition tells me that there is an energy that emanates from the body, which is beamed to the audience in the form of a vibration. Some feel this as a quiver in the spine. Although it is possible that the viewer, to some extent, may be predisposed to receiving a physical and emotional reaction to a famous star—that which transcends these expectations is what I refer to as "ki."

To illustrate this point, there is the following story about Leonard Bernstein, the noted American conductor, pianist and composer, who was invited to direct the Berlin Philharmonic Orchestra. This orchestra, led by the charismatic, fabled Austrian conductor Herbert von Karajan, was one of the world's greatest orchestras. The orchestra members, all the crème de la crème, would doubtless perform faultlessly and effortlessly under another director, but such performances would not move any mountains.

Bernstein took the podium. The members of the orchestra were outwardly composed and polite, but in their hearts they looked upon this young director rather lightly. As they began to play their instruments under Bernstein's direction, however, they underwent a remarkable change together. One by one they were caught up, both mind and soul, in Bernstein's inspired direction. They displayed the outer limits of their energy, and in no time they belonged to Bernstein.

It proved to be a performance of unprecedented excellence in the history of the Berlin Philharmonic Orchestra. It became a CD sold worldwide, with this story included in the commentary accompanying the disk. Bernstein's feat suggests a remarkable life energy.

Special Breathing Principles are the Source of Life Force

I'm convinced that special breathing methods are the all-important generator of life force. During my long search for answers, I became aware that gifted artists had a peculiar way of breathing and that it seemed to be the key that enabled them to elevate their life energy and exhibit the extraordinary abilities that gave them recognition.

To further seek answers about the origins of life force, after age fifty I took up martial arts. So perfect an expression is ballet that it seemed to me to be the epitome of Western physical culture. However, since it originated in the West, I sought something altogether different—for more universal principles and hence I turned my eyes to the East. I recognized that a disciplined self-pursuit and traditional Oriental culture are bound up in the martial arts, investing them with clues to understanding the secrets of physical and spiritual energy. Benefiting from my physical abilities acquired through ballet, it was with uncustomary speed that I was appointed an aikido master and awarded the highest level of certification in kung fu.

But I wasn't content with the traditional study of technique and spiritual discipline, and continued to seek out on my own the underlying principle that governs the power and grace that transcends training and technique.

Eventually my collective studies in medicine, ballet, and the martial arts led to my discovery of the principle I'd been seeking for so long—what I call *sokushin* breathing, or "sole-of-the-foot breathing." I discovered it at a moment of intense physical challenge.

One day during aikido practice, a higher ranked opponent skillfully engaged me in a surprise reverse move that might have overpowered me. At that instant, and without conscious effort, I drew in air through the soles of my feet and threw over my opponent. Stunned, I saw then that it was this power of the breath—the fundamental force that I had been searching for—that gives people their life energy. I spent the next few years exploring this way of breathing, the details of which would make another book. Suffice to say, however, that by the time I had developed the NBM, I was no longer interested in advancing my skills through aikido.

Taiki Activates the Body

In our classroom at the Nishino School, we do about an hour of basic training in breathing followed by about an hour of *taiki*. Taiki literally means exchange of ki energy. The student and instructor exchange ki by placing the backs of their hands together.

Through the hands, one transmits the entire body's ki to the other person. As one improves, however, one can send energy into the other person's body directly even without touching the hands.

When the ki of two people collide, the weaker ki will rebound. That is why many people who receive ki from their instructors are thrust backward involuntarily. As their ki becomes strong, and if they are still overpowered by their instructors, the rebound effect will be stronger, making them reel or "fly" or manifest some other strange and wonderful reaction. They are not thinking when the energy enters their bodies; nature and the body rejoice. Quantum theory states that the elementary particles that make up the body's cells are comprised of vibrating energy. When the body receives a strong input of energy, the vibrations are aligned and amplified, and hence setting off various reactions. In that moment when ki passes through the body, one feels inexpressibly good, and in fact some students laugh uncontrollably.

The author can send energy directly into the other person's body even without touching hands.

Receiving ki energy feels good, and it brings beneficial changes in the body and in life.

The French philosopher Henri Bergson considered laughter an important human trait. Why we laugh is still not well understood in physiological terms, but in recent years it has often been said that a natural unsolicited laugh has a favorable influence on the body. Laughs are of many kinds—temporizing laughs suited to the moment, socially expedient laughs, and so on. Laughter makes a very difficult study, but the natural, spontaneous laughter I'm able to generate through taiki is proof that the body is rejoicing in receiving ki energy.

The same reaction occurs when one eats something very delicious. In ancient times, before humans had acquired spoken languages, you can imagine those who

Feeling the ki.

The author demonstrates how he is able to emit ki from all sides.

Assistant Professor Katsunori Ikeda of Tokyo Gakugei University experiences taiki (ki exchange) for the first time.

The author and his instructors at the Nishino School demonstrate how ki travels through a line of people.

A special summer session of the Nishino
Breathing Method in Honolulu, Hawaii.

With journalist Shinichi Nemoto
during a taiki session.

A businessman during taiki.

With legendary diver Jacques Mayol, who
visits the Nishino School whenever he is in
Japan.

Giving a lecture at the 4th International
Congress on Traditional Asian Medicine
held in 1994 in Tokyo.

ate something delicious felt happy and how their faces naturally radiated joy. Eating is clearly a matter of energy entering the body. This flow of ki is a function of the universe and a natural human experience.

People watching a taiki session for the first time might think the participants are merely performing or are hypnotized. Not so. If such things were true, some 7,000 discerning people would not make time and pay their good money to commute for ki practice to the Nishino School. Many people come to the Nishino School because receiving ki energy makes them feel physically good and produces beneficial changes in their bodies and lives.

"Duende" Stimulates Creativity

Sokushin breathing is not a development from mental efforts or acquired knowledge. Rather, it is a method achieved through faithful physical practice. Since ki is an inherent fundamental energy that is beyond mental comprehension, I believe the only way to access it is through the body, or physical intelligence.

Sokushin breathing cultivates this physical intelligence, transmits ki energy throughout the body, and was developed as a way to increase the power of ki.

Later, I found that a few historical people both in the East and West had used breathing techniques that were similar to mine. One of them is the Russian ballerina Anna Pavlova, the finest ballerina at the beginning of this century whose performance of "The Dying Swan" was reputed to be magical and beyond imitation. Pavlova's *sur les pointes* gave the impression that she would remain motionless forever. Her pose just before the swan's death was said to be nothing short of miraculous. When asked about the secret of her *sur les pointes*, she replied, "I draw in air from the tips of my toes, slowly bring it up, then send it from my shoulders to the tips of my fingers so that my entire body feels like it is floating, and I can continue to keep the pose as long as I like."

Her exquisite pose was, we see now, sustained by her strange way of breathing from her toes. Many anecdotes about Pavlova linger on today. It's said that at the time she gave her performance in Japan in 1922, the acclaimed kabuki actor Rokudaime Kikugoro posed as a stage hand every night to spy on her and thus learn the secret of her breathing. It's a funny story—about one genius trying to learn the trade secrets of another.

The world-renowned Spanish flamenco dancer, choreographer and teacher Antonio Gades made a similar comment. "Among various things—gods and angels, for example—are some that cannot be explained with mere words. What can I say about my artistic activities? That they are entirely *duende* from beginning to end."

To performing artists *duende* has a meaning like the inspiration of life. The Spanish poet and dramatist Garcia Lorca said, "It comes up through the soles of the feet into and through the body. This spirit is black, but not evil. It is the power that stimulates the true struggle in the performing artist's creativity."

The Japanese have the expression "to feel at home on the boards." It originated in kabuki and is used to describe a performer who is physically pervaded with consciousness of the part, with feet planted firmly on the boards of the stage. It describes one who is performing brilliantly, with a firm grip on the part, carrying it out consummately. Conversely, the expression "feet not firmly planted on the earth" is applied to a performer who is nervous and unsettled.

To have consciousness in the soles of the feet, then, is an absolutely imperative condition for establishing a high-level physical body that can manifest innate power.

Harmonizing the Mind and Body at a High Level

You might be interested to learn a phrase related to breathing that originated over 2000 years ago in the Oriental classics and abounds in suggestions about breathing. The sage Chuang-tsu, who advocated a leisurely, natural life, said, "A pure person breathes through his heels, and an ordinary person breathes through his throat."

Truly developed people are those who grasp the essence of principles, or in other words, grasp the absolute without being carried along by time and tide. In my view, such people possess their own resolute physical intelligence without being manipulated by the mind, or conventional wisdom. Chuang-tsu meant that such people breathe deeply through the soles of the feet, whereas ordinary people, that is, people easily influenced by surrounding conditions—media, fashion, social conventions, etc.—breathe shallowly through their throats.

Although these words seem to express a sweeping philosophical approach to life, at their roots lie some shrewd insights into the human body. It would seem that the method of breathing through the soles of the feet has a fascinating point of physical-mental convergence, where ballet and flamenco pursue physical ability to its absolute limit on the one hand, and, on the other hand, a sage like Chuang-tsu pursues the boundaries of both mind and spirit in seeking to grasp the ultimate meaning of life.

In the East, there has been a tradition of training both mind and body through ascetic practices. The goal has been for the cultivation of character based on harmony of the physical and mental processes at a higher level. Put a different way, it is a method to unite physical and mental abilities so that one is able to do one's utmost when unexpected circumstance arises.

Among traditional ascetic practices one of the most persuasive is Zen. A leading contemporary figure in the movement, Sōjō Hirano, a chief priest at Zuigan Temple (a prime Zen training center) in Matsushima and a former Hanazono University professor, has been a student of mine for more than ten years. In 1992 Hirano published his book "Zen and Eastern Medicine," in which he introduced the NBM, characterizing it as being a method that can be mastered by anybody with immediate effects while similar to the old style of austerity practices in intent.

I might mention that there are several other students at the Nishino School who are Buddhist high priests, some from rigorously austere sects, who find my method of breathing beneficial.

Physical Intelligence and Life Energy

Thanks to the technological revolution, people have been using electricity and mechanical energy and hence enjoy lives of considerable convenience. Yet it is no exaggeration to say that the genre concerned with developing life energy that lies at the core of our lives and is essential to us is an almost entirely undeveloped sphere.

The NBM, through sokushin foot breathing, cultivates the physical intelligence that makes it possible to draw out potential abilities, whether they be mental or physical.

Developments in molecular biology, we now know, make possible communication of all kinds between cells. Scientists now refer to this as cellular intelligence. By combining sokushin breathing and taiki, the NBM develops the cellular level receptors necessary for the purpose of communication between cells and life energy.

In my breathing school many opera singers and artistic directors also practice sokushin breathing. Among them is Yukio Kitahara, the musical director of the Aachen Civic Opera once led by Karajan. Kitahara has been enthusiastically practicing the NBM for several years. Aachen, in western Germany near Belgium, was the second city of Charlemagne's empire and an important Roman spa. To become the director of its civic opera is a remarkable achievement even for a European and certainly for someone from another part of the world.

Kitahara achieved this honor at the still young age of 35 through his remarkable technique and talent—but he also acknowledges that ki power cultivated through the Nishino technique is a factor in his success. When he began practicing the NBM several years ago, he was the assistant director of the Innsbruck Civic Opera Company. But deciding that it was essential to learn the NBM in order to become a great conductor, he practiced sokushin breathing on his own every day without fail while in Europe.

When he returned to Japan to give regular performances with the NHK Symphony Orchestra, he always attended the Nishino School for taiki practice.

I referred earlier to Bernstein's fantastic energy, but Kitahara for his part also learned from Bernstein. The fact that an artist like Kitahara could demonstrate through his performances all over the world the remarkable power of ki nourished by the NBM is indeed heartening.

Lessons on Breathing From Our Evolutionary History

Inherent human physical abilities are truly remarkable. Changing the way of breathing is essential for strengthening the life force at the source and to go beyond mediocrity. In the four-billion-year history of life, the most important event of all is the change in breathing—that is, from branchial respiration—breathing through the gills—to pulmonary respiration—breathing with the lungs. This conclusion was reached about twenty years ago by the late Shigeo Miki, who was a distinguished scholar in comparative anatomy and professor at Tokyo National University of Fine Arts and Music.

Miki theorized that in the development of life the major leaps within evolution were the years of transformation from the aquatic stage to the terrestrial stage during the past four hundred million years. Exactly what is signified by the fact that living creatures fetch up from the water to dry land? It is this: that the primitive breathing by gills that they developed to sustain life under water changed to lungs that would enable them to survive on land in an environment suffused with air.

Human offspring, during the nine months they spend in amniotic fluid within the mother's body, experience a sudden reemergence of an evolutionary process. After their fetal period, from the 32nd day for one week corresponding to the decisive transition from the acquatic stage to the terrestrial stage, the mother has morning sickness and may almost miscarry. This life-threatening change of body, reflecting our evolutionary history of life on this planet, is reenacted by each individual fetus within the mother's womb.

The gills are flat, involuntary muscles that developed in the earth's living creatures before the evolution of their central nervous system. Gill breathing involves the opening and closing of the gills synchronous with the admission and expulsion of water, a process controlled by the respiratory center in the hindbrain or medulla. This is a primitive system that does not involve conscious action.

Lung breathing is a step ahead in evolutionary development, as air enters and leaves the lungs with the motion of striated muscles that function voluntarily. When human beings breathe, their striated lung muscles are usually controlled by the respiratory center in the medulla and there is no need to do this consciously. Unlike lower animals that breathe through their gills, however, human beings can consciously control their respiratory center and freely speed up or slow down their breathing.

Imperative Now: A Revolution in Breathing

Exactly because human beings can control their breathing individually, they can develop physical intelligence.

Miki observes that in earlier times, artisans acquired, in the long process of apprenticeship, a special way of breathing in tandem with body movement that facilitated output of their best efforts. Thus the accomplished artisan incorporated the special way of breathing in his movement without conscious effort.

In Japan, too, breathing was considered. The characters for breathing has been used to refer to deftness, indicating that breathing was considered important in acquiring highly specialized skills.

For us humans, who are destined to live creative lives by manifesting latent abilities, ideal breathing needs to be learned and acquired. In this vein, it has been traditionally said in Japan that mastering breathing is the quintessence of life. We should not be surprised then that the quality of breathing is directly connected with the development of physical intelligence.

In today's stress-filled world, our consciousness becomes unfocused and our breathing tends to become more shallow. Precisely because that's the kind of world we live in, we must improve our breathing.

If in the four-billion-year history of life the transition from branchial respiration to pulmonary respiration brought with it an epochal leap forward biologically, we might also imagine a similarly spectacular development by improving on our current lung breathing—enabling people individually to achieve latent potential. Human history will doubtless take a dramatic turn. Even though humankind today is caught up in all kinds of problems, the world in the 21st century will surely transcend today's pessimistic expectations and bring forth abundance and happiness.

One of the most important tasks of all requiring our attention in the new century is education. It has been the key in advancing human society, but today the two pillars comprising education—mental development and physical development—have nearly lost their relationship, becoming disconnected spheres. We need to recognize anew the essence of learning that bridges the two fields of the mental and physical. I call that "ki cultivation" and for convenience we might call it "ki'ing up."

Ki'ing up, on another level, is "sensitivity education"— that is, it involves training our senses and sensibility, those aspects of our being that are ignored in our current systematized intellectual and physical training.

The German poet Goethe said, "Senses cannot err, but judgment can." Judgment is a mental activity that often proves unreliable. Sense, on the other hand, falls in the domain of physical activity, and as such doesn't veer far from the truth.

The need to develop the senses and sensibility has been spoken of since ancient times, but yet we still have no clear answers concerning how this should be accomplished. We think that we have no choice but to hope to be born with finely-tuned senses. But in believing this myth of determinism, people must simply finish out their lives, conforming to fate against their will.

Ki'ing up is changing the breathing pattern, and cultivating your senses by steadily building up life energy and bringing out sensitivity. Ultimately, I hope that my breathing method will be adopted so that ki education can serve as a link between and vitalize intellectual and physical pursuits.

3

Creating
an Intelligent
Body

The NBM exerts a powerful effect and is, more than anything else, a practical method. Since it is instructive, I'd like to briefly cover the importance of the breath across different cultures.

Even were we to be unaware of the concept of ki, by simply living and breathing, we can literally feel the existence of ki with our skin. Ki is manifested in every aspect of our everyday life. You might already know, for example, that in India this energy is called prana.

In China, attitudes concerning ki's relationship to life and the universe were cultivated long and fully. Ancient Chinese thought held that ki was analogous with the vapors and gases present before the earth's creation, and hence connected ki with the universe. (The fact that this perception about the gaseous condition during the creation of the universe accords with the conclusions of Western science is interesting.) In this philosophy, ki was viewed as both the vast energy that filled the universe and also the body's internal energy. The Chinese philosopher Mencius, who coined the phrase "kōzen no ki," which means to revive spent energy, posited that ki is an energy that guides human life, opening it to the cosmos so that little, self-centered matters can be transcended and wider horizons met.

气
ki
↓
氣
ki
↓
気
ki

Not surprisingly then, there is a word for breathing in China that reflects this philosophy. The original Chinese character indicated steam or the breath moving upward. Thereafter it was modified and came to refer to ki energy. Inherent in the meaning of the character is "life" and "the source of actions." Thus the ideogram for breathing suggests the generation of ki energy.

In Europe, on the other hand, the Ionian school of natural studies (of the 6th to 5th centuries B.C.) used the word "psyche" as the breath-like animating principle of life. "Psyche" was a Greek term (pronounced *pu-shu-ke*) meaning "breath," and in time took on the meaning "soul" or "spirit." Thus, "breathing" is inherent in the flesh, bound up with a universal power that transcends it.

In practical terms, manifesting innate potential refers to demonstrating one's abilities with the addition of one's unique "super" power. To generate large-scale abilities while imprisoned in one's own narrow shell is impossible. We stay alive by absorbing cosmic energy within a vast universe. Human life could not exist without the cosmos; we are alive through cosmic grace. What we call breathing is taking in universal energy.

Inhalation and expiration is a state of regular exchange of internal and external energy. Hence breathing deeply, taking in universal (external) energy as much as we can, and thereby increasing our own (internal) energy, and manifesting that energy, is pleasingly logical.

In this connection, we might recall that breathing (assimilating external or cosmic energy) is called inspiration—the drawing of air into the lungs—and also denotes spiritual inspiration, heaven-sent brainstorms, clever ideas, "idea instilling," excitement, and so on—all the things that signify latent power. "Breathing," it is clear, is the basis for motivating people at the source and for drawing out their abilities.

Paradigm Shift: From Mind to Ki

Humans live in an ever dynamic temporal dimension. As a living organism filled with energy, cultivating latent abilities, this temporal aspect is very important. Although in the martial arts and in sports physical strength is measured linearly in concrete, mechanistic terms (weight x speed), or by chronological age, it is not that simple to summarize. We know, for example, that mechanical measurements are never an accurate prediction of competition results. We must factor in organic life force, which is the basis for human power and strength, within dynamic, ever-moving time.

Mental power is also an important factor. It is extremely great when the body is in balance, but when the body's balance is upset, mental power proves to be very fragile.

A famous professional golfer who is a close friend of mine once said, "What applies the brakes is the mind. When we're very close to a winning putt, various thoughts crowd our minds and our feet lose all their sensation. Our sense of balance is lost and our shoulders tighten up. Of course, if we settle down, it would be good . . . but it's hard to do."

As a professional player, my friend is obviously skilled and has a steely mental composure. If he didn't, how could he remain a top pro? However, when it comes right down to it, this emotional strength is less dependable than we think.

Some ten years ago in Japan a senior Zen priest, who was much admired by the younger priests under his charge, learned that he had cancer, and he subsequently committed suicide. The essence of Zen is a very physical-oriented training. Today, though, there is much emphasis on the mental aspect. If the mind were truly able to fortify us against severe duress, then surely such tragic events would not occur.

My point here is that the measure of human strength, the commonly perceived physical as well as mental aspects, can only be an informed guess at best. But we can come much closer to a realistic appraisal—and recognition of it—if we take as a basis "the open body," an organism embracing the cosmos with a positive exchange of energy within dynamic time. Reinforcing the "mental" aspect will only result in a further dichotomy of the mind and the body. Which brings me, therefore, to the conclusion that the era of the metaphysical soul or mind has passed its time and that we are now entering a new era of ki.

When I refer to ki, I'd like to point out several distinctions about this energy. First, ki should not be equated with the mental will or intention to do something or other forms of resoluteness, with which it might be mistakenly associated. If we talk about the "will" or "intention" at all, it is based on the physical body and thus spontaneous and natural.

Ki, as it is referred to in the Nishino School, is above all the ki of life energy. It should not be confused with the "primitive ki" or undeveloped (low-level) ki that every person naturally possesses—we call it the "insufficient" (mi-jūsoku) ki as opposed to the "sufficient" (jūsoku) ki in the NBM. Everything in the world that receives life gives off ki energy. This includes wild grasses and flowers, and animals. As living organisms, human beings, not least, possess a very large store of energy. Most people, however, simply don't notice it—or generate it. Feeling heat or a subtle emission of "something" from one's palm are phenomena that occur as a matter of course. I'd like to avoid thinking that such things are mystical or anything akin to supernatural power.

Furthermore, besides different levels of ki, such as undeveloped and developed (controlled, high-level) ki, there are qualitative differences in ki. For example, when a snake fixes its hypnotic gaze on a frog and the frog freezes where it sits, we see "primitive" ki in action. When primitive ki matures, it is not abnormal or sick but strong and pure. (Primitive ki that develops abnormally, as a result of poor circulation and imbalance in the mental-physical body, becomes "polluted" and commonly manifests as evil or sick behavior.) Mature or natural ki is healthy and life-affirming; it nourishes the nervous system and the brain so that our mental body will harmonize with our physical body on a high level, constantly drawing out innate talents and abilities. This is the kind of ki manifested by geniuses and saints who left their mark on our remarkable human history. In our current era, where we can begin with the premise of human equality, we must understand that each and every one of us is capable of nourishing this "right" ki. The NBM, in facilitating the development and control of this form of ki, refers to this type as "sufficient ki" (*jūsoku no ki*).

Think of ki as an intelligent energy that works together with science to open up new worlds. The role of science is in helping us to comprehend the mysterious, that is, with the intellect, and the role of ki is to illuminate the mysterious with the understanding from our bodies; both contribute to the development of society and culture through its practical power.

In between heaven and earth, humans live a pretty much self-centered, narrow-focused life. Although many of us believe that we live entirely by our own powers from birth, this is a rather skewed view of the world. In truth, we live embraced and nourished between two great energy fields, with the potential to expand beyond the limited perception we hold of our physical and mental selves.

As an example, let's take a look at why humans stand erect. The reason they can remain stable in a standing position is that the basic physical requirements for ensuring that condition have been previously established. Put another way, the physical laws that are already in place establishes the way we conduct our lives; we do not stand upright by our own volition. Outside the Earth's gravitational pull, the body will float freely in weightless space. No wonder astronauts who have set foot on the moon have changed their way of looking at life.

While in space, these astronauts experienced all kinds of uncommon abilities. Why? we may well wonder. Ancient Chinese philosophy can help us in this regard. Chinese Taoists formulated a model of the universe based on five energy phases and their movement on the macrocosmic and microcosmic level. This philosophy refers to the nature of materials as well as their interrelationships. Each phase, symbolized by an element, represents a category of related energy functions and properties, including color, organ of the body, emotion, direction, season, and so forth. In the context of our discussion of ki, these phases express different qualities of ki.

To illustrate the importance of a certain quality of ki,

let me give the example of the seasons of nature. Of the symbolic elements—wood, fire, earth, metal, water—four of them—wood, fire, metal and water—correspond to the four seasons—and to different qualities of ki. This model formulates the cyclical transformation of ki as observable in nature. Both winter and summer, and spring and autumn, are in yin-yang relationship (two components of a relationship that accounts for changes in the universe). From the yin of water we enter the cheerful activities of spring (yang of wood), and then go on to sunny summer. Autumn, too, is yin, from which we have the withering state of nature and enter the extreme yin of winter.

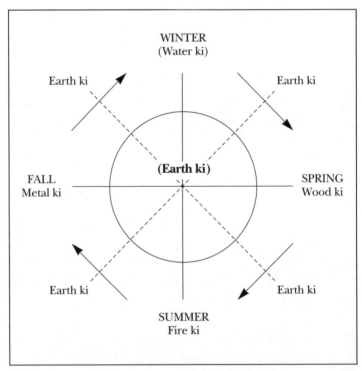

The five energy phases and different qualities of ki in our world.

THE BREATH OF LIFE

The changes of these four seasons do not occur abruptly. During each season there are transitional periods leading up to the next season. These are the days of "earth." The earth ki is associated with balance and neutrality, and thus, functions to stimulate the seasonal cycles, of changing all things to earth, and to nurture all things to maturity. Seasons pass on—each season with its special ki—and a new season introduced, and the year goes by without a hitch; a cycle is completed.

Observing and following the natural laws of "earth ki" means going with the flow of life. This "flow" is another variation of the theme of "fluctuation," which we covered earlier in Chapter 1, where we must respect our bodies natural desire for changeability.

Embodying the Principles of the Universe and of Life

In the Japanese writing system the word for "person" or "human body" is composed of the character for person (*hito* or *nin*) and the character for between or among (*aida, kan, gen*): hence, together, it is *ningen*, meaning "between or among people." To each individual the "between" or "among" factor—that is, relations with other people—is essential. A way of living worthy of being human means to open oneself to others and safeguard one's relationships. Closing oneself is not a normal, wholesome way to live, nor should life's wonders be shut out.

人間
nin gen

The body is an open system, so to manifest its latent properties should be natural and life-affirming. Breathing is what directly symbolizes this system. Its process stimulates the circulation of the body's life energy with the outside world through an internal-external exchange of gas. Closing off the body means not breathing, that is, exchanging energies with the world around us.

While it isn't possible to have a closed system as long as we are alive, unless one breathes well, one cannot lead an active, positive life. Poor or incorrect breathing, which brings about an inadequate oxygen supply to the brain, will result in an attempt to shut down the body. . . . In the final stages, by the time adulthood is reached, the body is controlled by intellectual processes.

This is because brains that are placed under excessive stress and thus suffer lowered performance levels shut-down in the face of information overload. The body, governed by the brain, can no longer receive outside input as it was originally intended to do. Typically, this manifests as aging, where there is a body-mind imbalance. This is the common phenomenon we see in our mental-centered society of information glut.

Aging—I refer here to mental aging,—is manifested first of all in being inordinately taken up with custom and "common sense." One's way of looking and thinking about things begins to lack flexibility.

People are born pliant and then harden and die. I'm referring here to the physical body, but essential factors concerning a person's body inevitably exerts an influence on the mind. Ways of thinking and feeling that become rigid are indeed manifestations of an aging organism. Not surprisingly, then, do the elderly tend to become inflexible in their thinking.

Commonly, those who we refer to as "geniuses" have young minds and can always accommodate fresh new ideas no matter what the circumstances. The meaning of a child's having a fresh, youthful body gleefully receptive to various wonders is all a kind of genius. Well depicted in Michael Ende's topical "Momo," also made into a film, was this very broad-scale tolerance, innocent and pliant, based on a child's body and sensitivities. "Momo" is a children's fable, and as usually the case in such first-rate productions one always finds a hint of the truth.

There is an expression in Zen, "yuge-zanmai," which refers to the condition of playing innocently like a child. It typifies the most liberated type of person. To be sure, to children, not being locked in to common sense, playing is living itself. Their supple young bodies and natural curiosity will always be their learning tools, nourishing creative intelligence.

Thus, we can say that the beginnings of intelligence lie first of all in feeling with a body as pure and innocent as a child's. We might further assume that this intelligence is above all one that is in accord with natural providence and the fundamental principles of life—and one that the NBM considers of paramount importance as we enter a new century, that is, the intelligent body.

Developing the Body's Vision

So what, exactly, is this "intelligent body"? I am referring to a particular cellular state in which the five senses function optimally to receive outside stimuli. As mentioned, each individual cell—all 60 trillion of them—possesses an intelligence. Although science has still not been able to explain the mechanism of how one primordial cell differentiated into the mind-boggling number that make up the human body, we can posit that each cell has inherited a form of intelligence from that single cell 4 billion years ago. Not only that, each cell has the potential ability to become any one of those trillions of specialized cells.

The Russian-born American pianist Vladimir Horowitz had fingertips that seemed to "hear," feel the music, and play the piano. The German composer and pianist Ludwig van Beethoven, even after losing his hearing, was able to feel inspired with his entire being and thus compose moving music.

In the same way, by developing my body in ballet and the martial arts, independent parts of my body could sense varied conditions and cope. This indeed is discovering a case of "One is everything and everything is One" in a cellular sense. Each cell is a microcosm of the intelligent body.

When I first discovered the breathing method, both my hands became like sensitive antennae—as if they were high-performance sensors. Soon my entire body became like a sensor and I could sense others' movements, whether I touched them or not.

Through my body, those around me were revealed. This kind of revelation is fundamentally different from a visual one. If one trusts only the visual sense, sports and, to think in martial arts terms, feints and other tactical techniques would be difficult to avoid.

The turn-of-the-century French artist Paul Cézanne is one who thought visual sense was suspect. His contemporary, the English artist and archaeologist William Collingwood, said that Cézanne's genius was manifested in his still-life designs, which appeared to have been felt with the palm of his hand.

The Swiss sculptor and painter Alberto Giacometti also spoke of Cézanne's work in a similar vein: "The way I see it, Cézanne throughout his life continuously sought depth." Cézanne's 'depth' is not something simply grasped by the visual senses. Rather, it is altogether a depth grasped with the tactile sense."

The sense of touch is a basic form of perception that takes in our very existence. Speaking from the standpoint of the NBM, Cézanne may be said to have seen with the entire body—what I call the "body's eye." In the NBM it is not the training of the specific senses but the activation of all the body's cells that brings out the body's overall abilities. Thus, anyone can create a physical vision or "body's eye."

Cultivating a Pure and Innocent Body

The Japanese haiku poet Kyoshi Takahama wrote, "Be awed by the morning snow and aspire to verse. Without this sensitivity, this capacity to be moved and to be filled with wonder, neither intelligence nor the arts would evolve. To be moved is the very joy and pleasure of living itself; the fountain of wisdom.

The moment an infant's eyes open, the joy of its entire body is apparent; through physical movements, an infant exults, "I'm alive!" In this fundamental form of intercourse with the world lies the source of learning and of "knowing."

Eventually at some point in growth, the impressions and sense of wonder will manifest not only through the physical body but through words—language.

It is one of our fundamental characteristics, and yet, no matter how words may inundate, or confuse us, they never fall into disuse. Our lexicons never vanish.

However, words can also be the main hindrance to our growth. The Austrian philosopher Ludwig Wittgenstein, who placed a special emphasis on linguistics and epistemology, said, "Philosophy is a battle against the spell that words have over the intellect."

Language is a relative medium of communication. It is inexact in that no matter how precise we try to be in our words, they are always open to different interpretations by others. But language can be given an element of universality. Meaning carries over across different lands, cultures, sub-cultures, and individuals by dint of physical instinct—or what I call the physical body. While our minds produce the words, our best and wisest interpretation of them comes from the depth of our being. They give language an inherent absoluteness, a ring of truth, so to speak, that can only be recognized when we listen to our physical organism.

Just as individual geniuses pre-exist within our bodies, words are the manifestation of a marvellous physical nature that encompasses all that is associated with the human senses and sensitivity. Our "good sense" implicitly means the full use of all the five senses and the "sixth sense" as well. It is by no means the exclusive possession of people having a special mental facility.

In his *Discourse on Method* the French philosopher and mathematician René Descartes said that "good sense" is the most equitably distributed thing in existence. I am firmly convinced that Descartes' "good sense" is making reference to a naive body, one with good judgmental powers based on sufficient ki circulating throughout it.

To treat our modern pathology of separated mind

Good ki circulation is the basis for full use of the senses, or cultivating excellent ones.

and body we must first of all recover the inherent ability of the body. An intelligent body, in time, will cultivate good sense. The NBM is conceived for that purpose.

**To Know Oneself is to
Create Oneself**

The wonder of the human body is that it has an active and creative quality, allowing experiences of new personal potential. The French word for body, "corps," originates from the Latin word "corpus," which incorporated the meaning "to create" from "creo." "Creo" itself hails from the Sanskrit word "kar," which means to create.

I make this linguistic note because the link between the body and creativity is important. The French poet Paul Valéry, known for his insights into the human body, believed that the philosophy holding the human body fundamentally unimportant was ludicrous and held the view, instead, that the body was a one-of-a-kind, true, eternal, and whole system.

Valéry devised a model for the human organism called an "implexe," which included potential abilities, using the analytical skills of the Descartists. The essential point of his model was the realization of every moment of individual human existence and all its potential, which serves as the basis for dynamic change.

Valéry's "implexe" body shows the influence of Freud's theories on the complex in the realm of the subconscious. In contrast to subconscious drive—those hidden agendas deep within us, however, the "implexe" body allows people to feel, react, act, and comprehend as pure potential beings.

In Buddhism it is recognized that the limited real world of "being" is enveloped by the unlimited world of "non-being" or emptiness. Similarly, we can use our mind, or self-awareness, to grasp discouragingly little about our bodies. As a microcosm of the universe with unlimited potential, we cannot know it through the vehicle of the mind.

Just as one cannot know the flavor of food without tasting it, the body is discovered not through words and concepts but by being sentient. Unfortunately, most of us are not fully sentient beings, little aware of our bodies while believing that we understand them.

How should the body, then, be understood? I believe it should be developed consistently with the way the body feels.

In this regard, we can look to Eastern wisdom for their contribution toward asceticism or esoteric physical training, while Western wisdom focused on linguistic knowledge. Western wisdom's ultimate expression is Socratic, based on the teachings of the Greek philosopher in the fifth century B.C. The central theme of Socrates' teachings and writings was the quest for truth by first recognizing that we knew nothing. We come closer to the truth through this paradox—the more we know, the more convinced we become that we know nothing.

Language is an incredible resource of human wisdom. In the course of its development it inspired the birth of science and brought about astonishing historical progress. But in the sense of grasping the meaning of one's own existence, it cannot be denied that language proves to be a roundabout method.

Oriental sages seeking the truth about themselves rather than social development pursued the acquisition of knowledge through ascetics. By taking one's own physical body, I believe any person can know the truth about his own existence. By "know" in this context I mean something different from cognitive knowledge of course. The brain and the body are united and the breadth and depth of "knowing" is directly connected to the qualitative experience of life.

Acquiring this "knowing," however, as evident looking back in history, is by no means a simple matter. One must take the body in its natural condition, just as it is, and by training, elevate it to a high-level organism. In yoga and esoteric Buddhism severe ascetic practices are required. This is pointedly expressed in the Sanskrit word "tapas" for "practice," translated as penance or asceticism.

A present-day form of ascetics that any person can practice is my breathing method. By providing exercises with a clear-cut method, the breathing techniques I developed make possible basic ascetic-like training of the body without the need for rigorous practices.

In fact, the original meaning of the "tapas" is "to heat things" as in the procreative warmth of a chicken nestling to hatch its chicks. As one who spent many years in the creative world of ballet, I knew with my body that true creativity can only arise from within physical warmth and placidity.

The knowing body means nothing other than a body based on the principle of "know thyself" and "create thyself."

CHAPTER 4

The Essence of Sokushin Breathing

That breathing nourishes and brightens all kinds of life organisms is quite natural—and yet often overlooked. Let's briefly review the origins of life. Twenty billion years ago the universe began, according to our best guess, with the Big Bang. On the Earth, a planet in the solar system lying within a tiny nook of the universe came into being 4 billion years ago. These small living systems, or cellular structures, contain tiny cylindrical-shaped bodies called mitochondria. So long as the cellular structure continues to function, these mitochondria carry out important fermentation and are places where energy is generated. If we say that "In the beginning there were words," then, it means that "In the beginning there was breathing." (Strictly speaking, it was fermentation, but by the time words came about it was breathing!)

生
live

+

息
breath

=

生き生き

When life is defined in biology and other sciences, breathing is above all a basic consideration, usually followed by such other factors as metabolism (growth), proliferation, and genetics. In Japanese, the characters for "live" and for "breath" are homophones pronounced "iki" because they have the same etymological derivation. To be living, in other words, means to be breathing. By repeating the character for "live" (iki) we have the Japanese word "iki-iki," which means vigorous or energetic, but in fact it signifies very active breathing.

Infants have ideal breathing habits. They breathe very deeply. As one enters adulthood, breathing becomes more shallow. Adults utilize the respiratory capacity and lung capacity to the extent necessary. Quite a bit of breathing ability is held in reserve and remains unused.

Deep breathing increases the lungs' function, and as oxygen is consumed correspondingly and pervades the body, the entire body's cells are activated to an extent much greater than before.

The NBM uses not only breathing by the lungs (that is breathing whereby external air is drawn into the trachea and the air then enters the lungs, oxygen enters the bloodstream, and carbon dioxide is expelled) but breathing with the entire body so as to apply its benefits throughout. It ensures that oxygen that enters the bloodstream goes to all the body's structural cells, where oxygen is released and carbon dioxide from the structural cells is taken into the bloodstream. If breathing efficiency is improved, it seems only scientific and natural that potential ability is steadily drawn out.

Drawing in Air from the Feet

The soles of the feet have always been regarded as the second heart in traditional Oriental medicine and are an important part of the body in the context of respiration. While the heart functions as a pump so that blood circulates throughout the body, to send it back to the heart from the soles of the feet—located farthest from the heart and at the point that receives the body's full weight—is no small task. It is necessary of course to carry out the minimal gas exchange involved in sustaining human life (i.e., supplying oxygen and expelling carbon dioxide) but also to improve the blood circulation if only a little and admit plenty of oxygen so that the body can function close to optimum levels. The second pump can be considered the soles of the feet in helping the heart to carry out its task.

The basis for the NBM is sokushin breathing, or "sole-of-the-foot breathing," which I've already mentioned, and chūyū (incorporating the concepts of kanyō and sennen discussed earlier).

足心
soku shin

足芯
soku shin

So what does sokushin breathing entail? "Sokushin" is Japanese for the sole of the foot. There is a Chinese word with the same meaning, but the character used in it for the "shin" of "sokushin" refers to the soul. This is a matter of fine distinction in meaning. In the Nishino School, the character meaning "core" or "center" of a plant is used for "shin" to convey the physical aspect of the term. Thus, sokushin refers to the central part of the foot. The NBM requires breathing from the soles of the feet as a way to draw energy in to circulate through the entire body and then to push it out from the soles of the feet.

Envision a plant or large tree drawing up water and nourishment with its roots—the soles of your feet. Breathe in long and carefully—of course you actually breathe through your nose—but when you breathe with conscious awareness of the soles of the feet, you can feel the ki energy rising up . . . from the soles to the knees . . . to the thighs . . . and then to the *tanden,* a focal point at the center of lower abdomen about 3 centimeters below the navel (*tan-tien* in Chinese).

After you draw up energy to the tanden, it is important to bring a subtle awareness to the anus, at the base of the spine. This will help you to avoid becoming tense and getting an unsettled feeling should you try to breathe too hard. Also, the act of breathing is more clearly perceived. From the anus, the energy is then drawn up along the

Sokushin breathing begins, first, by taking in air through the nose with conscious awareness of the soles of the feet.

The breath is taken through the spine and up to the crown of the head, where it is held briefly.

spine, the passage for the nerves of the spinal cord.

Through the spine, the energy reaches the top of the head at the site of the anterior fontanelle in the infant, the soft spot that moves with breathing. When the energy reaches the top of the head, the breath is held momentarily. Next, the energy is then pushed down quickly back to the tanden—along a central line in the front of the nose, mouth, throat, and chest. Then during exhalation, the energy is directed down to the soles of the feet, and finally into the ground.

Ki is circulating in the body in conjunction with breathing. By mastering this process, you can begin to feel clearly that the soles of the feet are breathing in as an actual function of the body. Beginners may not sense it at first, but before thinking about it and becoming anxious, simply do it and let your body get used to it. Even those who don't develop this facility quickly will get it down in two or three months—a deep, smooth breathing entirely different from the shallow breathing done with the lungs.

In both China and Japan a popular fixture since ages ago is what the Japanese refer to as a *takefumi* (tah-keh-fu-mih), an object made of individually cut sections of a large round bamboo pole split down the middle and cut into uniform lengths, to enable one to stand on them and massage the soles of the feet. This practice is recognized as being good for the health because stimulating the soles of the feet is extremely effective in promoting blood circulation. Sokushin breathing, though, is not external stimulation but internal; it is consciously feeling the soles of the feet and tapping your body's reservoir of energy.

In short, it involves consciously circulating your breath

throughout your body so that your system can store up, for use at any time, the energy force that is essential for a full, active life.

Human beings alone have an upright gait. Why? In the words of the internationally famous specialist on monkeys, Kinji Imanishi, "human beings stand upright because they need to."

In fact, why human beings stand upright is something of an enigma. At the very least, it seems to me to symbolize the mysterious nature of the human body.

Quadrupeds are said to have the same body axis as the direction of movement. Four-footed animals, being parallel to the earth, move in that direction. To these animals, events on the earth's surface are everything.

But what about human beings? Our axis is clearly different from other animals. Being perpendicular to the ground, our movements are not limited to the earth's surface but, rather, open up to the world all around us. We look toward the heavens for infinite possibilities.

Indeed, we've invented aircraft to soar the skies, and rockets to explore uncharted space. In some sense, the human upright gait is a metaphor for the desire—and necessity—to transcend the everyday physicality of life on earth; we are not content simply to be connected to events on the earth's surface. We have our own ideas and desires that transcend our real world.

Our lofty ideas must be grounded on the earth, however. After all, we go through life with our feet planted upon the earth. If we separate ourselves from this bond—this link with the earth—we plunge ourselves into uncertainty.

We must, then, find the strength of action to have a firm basis on earth and a secure reality, while at the same time seek our essence with unlimited curiosity, passion, and desire for self-development.

To the original question "Why did human beings become erect?" I propose looking at the mystery of the human animal from a physical point of view. Humans must live oriented toward both heaven and earth and circulate energy. The breathing exercises we do at the Nishino School epitomize this circulation of energy from the earth to the heavens and back through sokushin breathing, making the most of our upright stance.

A Window Into the Future Through Holistic Breathing

The scientific method, of discovering universal laws of nature has had an immeasurable influence on the development of civilization and culture. I think ballet embodies this progress beautifully. Supported by a well-defined syllabus, ballet is the culmination of machine-like thoroughness, the art and essence of technique. When one carries out this training to the limit, the body exhibits individualism for the first time. This is the philosophy applied by the legendary ballet master George Balanchine in nurturing his ballerinas.

As one might guess, there is still another supporting factor required in the development of a ballet dancer, namely, a highly artistic sense. But to establish this esthetic sense, above all a body that functions like a precision instrument is necessary. I fully experienced ballet's precision training, but when I subsequently mastered the essence of traditional Japanese martial arts in aikido, I recognized their contrasting methods.

I believe the best method for developing the body in the 21st century must incorporate both the implicitness of Buddhist methods and of the martial arts and the explicit ways of science. It should be holistic; rationally clear and yet profound. It must answer clearly the question, "How can we best breathe?"

Breathing was considered very important in the world of Zen. Priest Keizan (1268–1325), founder of the Sōtō sect of Zen sect and successor to Dōgen, said:

"If you want to practice zazen it is important to develop correct breathing. When practicing zazen, if you feel heat or cold, or you experience excessive tension, or conversely, indolence, it means your breathing is not regulated. Regulating it is necessary. Open your mouth only very slightly. Long breaths are made by breathing long and short breaths by breathing short.

"When one practices zazen while breathing serenely, it creates an absorption with nature and a state of selflessness, and breathing, too, becomes even and regulated, without conscious effort. . . . During the process of practicing ascetics, consciousness becomes indistinct and one hallucinates, about Buddha and Buddhist saints, or of having become completely enlightened in the Buddhist scriptures—but this is not a benefit of zazen but rather a ki-related malady that requires regulation of one's ki (i.e., breathing)."

Communicating the importance of this "breathing" in

Zen fell to the Zen priest Hakuin (1685–1768), founder of the Rinzai school of Zen. He writes about the secret techniques used for his austerities:

"If you think you wish to study this esoteric tantric Buddhism, for a while you should stop meditations and empty the mind of kōan riddles. First of all get a good sleep and awaken fresh. Just before falling asleep extend both legs, and send your entire body's energy from your lower abdomen below the navel to the hips and legs and all the way to the arches of the feet. Then adhere to the following procedures.

(1) My abdominal region, hips, legs, and the soles of my feet are all part of my essential character.

(2) My abdominal region is my true source and as such it is always grounded.

(3) My abdominal region is the heart of me, and is a paradise, and cannot be separate from my mind and exist in another paradise.

(4) My abdominal region is the Amitabha [Buddhist saint] of everything within my body and to the extent that my body is an Amitabha it is not supposed to advocate Amitabhas other than its own.

Think repeatedly in this way."

Tantric Buddhism's regular flow of long and short breathing and its requirement for diligent practice remains a challenge, not only for lay people but for loyal followers. Also, verbal explanations, and thus universalization, of the Zen method, is not, in my view, something to be heavily relied upon. The best teachers are those who have assimilated the supreme "method" in the form of a supreme ki. Why? Because the abundant ki energy is transmitted to the learner's body and transforms without one's realization, becoming a guiding force from within. Sokushin breathing is quite clear and easy to practice, and the subsequent taiki (ki energy exchange) involves just this sort of non-verbal transmission, from instructor to student.

Breathing is the Spark of Yin and Yang

There have been many ki theories in the past developed by those who have come to know this primal energy. One, in particular, is of interest to us here. It is the *I Ching: The Book of Changes,* a work that predates Taoism and Confucianism. It postulates a grand design of the universe based on change. In this classic text, change is seen as the result of the interaction of two poles of the universal force (ki), which they called yin and yang. Ki oscillates between yin and yang, manifesting different qualities or phases of its energy.

In general, yin and yang is often interpreted as a type of dualism, in other words, as fixed, opposing forces or parts. But contrary to the Western idea of dualism, they are not confrontational or contradictory. While they exist separately, they hold a complementary relationship. They are relative, meaningful only in relationship to one another, not absolute.

"The presence of yin, the presence of yang, this is what is called the way" an ancient Chinese expression goes. Indeed, they are distinctly different and alternately exchange the leadership role while maintaining a balance together. Both meanings are evident in the way the expression is phrased.

One of the concrete manifestations of the interchange of yin and yang is "hard" and "soft." In ki terms, they are yin and yang, where hard is yang and soft is yin. The yin-yang or hard-soft are continually changing their composition, and thus the balance of their parts.

The idea of hard-soft and its interchange is one of the core principles of life, indeed the essence of changes in life itself. The true meaning of each concept cannot be brought out without the help of the other. For something to be truly "hard" it must be supported in some hidden way by a softness.

Architectural forms are examples. Soaring skyscrapers, combining our knowledge of science as well as functional beauty, evoke an image of "hardness" or strength. To support the weight of an awesome building that rises for several tens of floors in a comparatively small area—even against strong winds—requires structural "hardness." At the same time, it must be able to withstand the severe jolts of earthquakes; the energy must be diffused and absorbed by structural "softness," or flexibility. The life of a skyscraper is the very balance existing between the structural "strength" and the structural "softness."

Sofas and beds, too, are not good simply if they are soft. To ensure long hours of comfortable rest, they need their "gentle" softness to be reinforced with "strength."

Ballet, too, requires that top dancers have "hardness" within their "softness" and "softness" within their "hardness," and at times they draw forth unbelievable qualities of both.

In all kinds of actions, unless "hard" and "soft" harmoniously blend together, skills and abilities having tenacity and suppleness cannot come into being. And that which effects the interaction of "hard" and "soft" is, as mentioned in the *I Ching*, ki. When this dynamic interchange produces these skills and abilities, inevitably spirals are created. We can observe that outstanding dances and martial arts movements all feature spirals.

Spirals are sometimes called life-curves, perhaps the most recognizable example being the genetic arrangement and the molecular structure of DNA. The peculiar quality of the spiral is that when two interrelated elements that comprise it, such as "hard" and "soft," produce a movement, the dual characteristics cease; there is no "hard" or "soft," no inside-outside (frontside-backside) or left-right distinction. The Möbius strip illustrates this.

Breathing harmonizes yin and yang, in the way that a

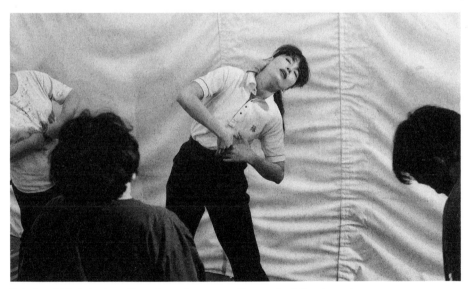

Spirals, which have tenacity and suppleness, are the result of the dynamic interchange of yin and yang.

spiral or the Möbius strip connects the inner and outer. Since antiquity in India's ascetic practices, "breathing" has been something that fused together the "internal" (human body = micro-universe) and the external (world = macro-universe) by connecting the "spirit" and the "flesh." When the ki created from this union, or breathing, is used to its optimal limit, confrontations stop being confrontations. The breath-infused yin and yang, the internal and external world, compose an energy balance that is in harmony with the universe.

CHAPTER 5

The Practice of the Nishino Breathing Method

Classes in the NBM consist of two fundamentals parts; one, various breathing exercises with the main focus on breathing through the soles of the feet, and second, exchanging ki energy, that is, taiki, with another person. I introduce here seven exercises that we always practice for the first part, which will prepare the way for taiki with a partner. While it isn't always possible to practice taiki, especially if you are alone or away from the Nishino School, simply doing the breathing exercises will bring immeasurable benefits by starting the process of cellular vitalization. Please remember, though, that daily, or at the least regular, practice of some of these exercises with a view toward the long-term is very important if you want to feel results.

First, with the preparatory exercise called *karin*, loosen and relax the body. Then carry out the sokushin breathing exercises in the following sequence: *tenyū*, *enten*, *gyōun*, *tenshoku*, *rengyō*, and *muhen*. It does not follow, however, that it is necessary to do all seven basic exercises. Rather than do all of them as a norm in a fixed regimen, it is better to do those you like at your own pace in a leisurely, enjoyable way.

There will be elements of kanyō ("loosening up") and sennen ("twisting," or more exactly, like stretching and twisting combined) in all the exercises. When doing kanyō and sennen, don't allow your body to go limp, but rather, twist naturally—with suppleness. In other words, loosening and twisting, the front and the back of the body function together in harmony. With practice, you will begin to enter a state of chūyū, in which the experi-

The element of Kanyō ("loosening up") is a part of this exercise.

Sennen, or twisting, too, is an important component of the preparatory exercises.

ence of ki circulating throughout the body will be a physical reality.

The Process of Breathing With Your Feet

Let me go over again briefly the process of sokushin breathing: inhalation is through the soles of the feet and, after energy has been circulated throughout the body, exhalation is, again, through the soles. In fact, you are breathing through the nose, but if you do so with an awareness of the soles of the feet, you will feel ki—that is, energy—rising upward from the feet to the knees and the thighs to the tanden or lower abdominal region.

Many of my students visualize a great tree sucking up water from the earth. Energy that reaches the tanden is steadily propelled upward along the spine. This energy in turn eventually reaches the *hyaku-e*, the crown of the head, a soft part of the head during infancy that moves very actively in synch with breathing.

At this point, lightly hold your breath, and then—still on the in-breath—send the energy from the crown through your nasal cavity, mouth, throat, chest, and entire body, frontally, along its central line, to the tanden. Finally, while exhaling, direct the energy downward through the soles of the feet into the earth.

Karin

華輪

Karin is a preparatory exercise for the Nishino Breathing Method. It loosens up the body and makes way for the ideal of "playing in the universe," thus enhancing the benefits of the breathing method.

With the knees slightly bent, the lower body from the navel down is comfortably stable supporting the upper body poised perfectly upright and relaxed. Without losing a sense of this axis, rotate your trunk gently while keeping awareness of energy in the tanden. This swinging on an axis should be done smoothly and calmly, without any force. The arms are loose but naturally resilient, wrapping or coiling round the body like a whip around a rod (but more gently of course).

Karin is done not with sokushin breathing but with normal inhaling and exhaling.

SET 1: Normal Swing ───────────────────────────

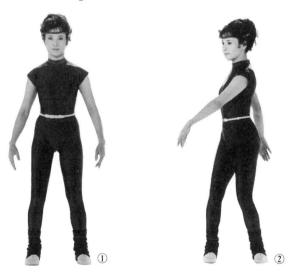

① Stand with the entire body relaxed, feet shoulder-width apart and knees slightly bent.

② Breathing out, gently swing to the right, rotating around the axis of the spine. Move from the tanden.

③   ④   ⑤

③ Let the arms, which are relaxed and loose, wrap around the body as a natural result of rotating the trunk.

④ In the same way, with the spine as the pivot, swing to your left.

⑤ This swing to the right and then left is one set. Repeat the set twenty to thirty times. Pay attention to the position of the hands and make sure the stability of the hips is maintained.

SET 2: Slap the Shoulders

⑥   ⑦

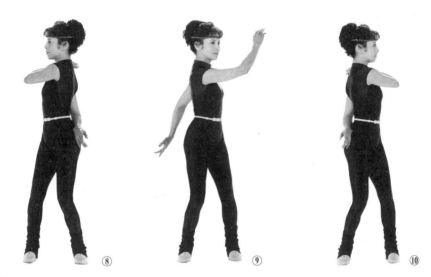

⑧ ⑨ ⑩

⑥ Continuing to rotate right and left, let your outside arm wrap around the shoulder.

⑦ Exhaling gently, rotate your trunk to the right, remembering to initiate the action with your tanden, not the arms.

⑧ Your left arm swings to your shoulder, while your right arm wraps around your hip. Try not to tense your shoulders. Keep heels firmly planted on the floor.

⑨ Repeat, swinging to the left.

⑩ Your right arm comes to the shoulder, while your left arm wraps around your hip. Repeat set 2 twenty to thirty times.

SET 3: Look at the Heels ———————————————

⑪ Maintain the same swinging motion.

⑫ With arms relaxed, turn your body to the right, initiating the movement from your tanden.

⑬ Without straining, look at the heel of the farthest leg. Arms wrap naturally around your body.

 ⑭

 ⑮

 ⑮'

⑭ Repeat to the other side.

⑮ Look at the heel of the farthest leg. Repeat set 3 twenty to thirty times.

⑯ Return to set 1 and let the motion come to a gradual stop, body completely relaxed.

 ⑯

天遊 *Tenyū*

This is one of the basic exercises of the Nishino Breathing Method. It is done in a spirit of childlike innocence, playing unfettered under the heavens. Releasing all tension from the body, both hands are used to guide sokushin breathing. When bending the body forward, the breath should be directed down to the soles of the feet.

With practice, improved blood circulation, as well as enhanced energy and stamina is possible.

 ①  ②  ②'

① Release all tension from the body and stand, knees relaxed, with the feet shoulder-width apart.

② While exhaling down toward the soles of the feet, slowly bring the upper body forward.

③ As you inhale from the soles of your feet, gradually bring your arms forward and up.

④ Lift both arms above your head and bring the breath to hyaku-e (the crown of your head), then hold briefly without straining and direct the breath down to your tanden.

⑤ While still holding the breath, bring both arms down, extending them wide on either side at shoulder level.

③

④

⑤

⑥ Slowly lower your arms to your sides as you exhale.

⑦ Breathing out, you return to the original starting position.

Enten 円天

This exercise relaxes the entire body. Taking a hint from the literal meaning of the two characters, visualize drawing a big circle in the heavens with your arms.

When breathing out, gently flex at your wrists as you lower your arms. Heels are pressed to the floor when squatting, and shoulders are relaxed, with arms extended comfortably forward. Movement is done with ankles and knees pliant. This is an effective exercise for lumbago.

① With the body—including knees—totally relaxed, stand with feet shoulder-width apart.

② Breathing from the soles of the feet, interlock your fingers, with your palms facing up.

③ Bring your hands to chest level and let it rest there while you continue to draw the breath to the crown of your head. Hold and direct the breath down to your tanden.

④

⑤

⑤'

④ Turn your palms inside out and begin to exhale.

⑤ Lower to a squat while you continue to breathe out. As you extend your arms in front of you, palms facing out, gently feel the stretch in your fingers.

⑥   ⑥'   ⑦

⑥ Come to an upright position as you breathe in again from the soles of your feet, lifting your arms and still-interlaced fingers. Make sure to keep shoulders free of tension.

⑦ Bring your arms above your head with your palms facing the sky, then hold the breath when it reaches the crown of the head; bring the breath down to your tanden. Release your fingers as you begin your exhale.

⑧ While slowly breathing out, flex at the wrist and carve an arc in the air with your arms as you let them float back down.

⑨ Continue to bring your arms down slowly to your sides.

⑩ Completing the exhale, you return to the starting position.

Visualize white clouds serenely traversing the sky to help you in this exercise. When you step forward with a bent knee, remember to keep the heel of your other foot pressed to the floor, and your inner arms together and extended comfortably in front of you. As you raise your arms above your head, keep your upper body, especially the shoulders, sufficiently loose and pliant. Keep the energy circulating even as you bend forward in a tight position. *Gyōun* relieves fatigue, energizing the physical body.

① In a relaxed state, stand with one foot in front of the other, shoulder-width apart.

② Raise both arms, elbows bent and hands with palms facing up, to chest level while inhaling from the soles of your feet. Draw the breath to the crown of your head, then direct it down to your tanden.

③ While exhaling, take a large step forward with the leg in front. Bring the back of your hands together and extend them in front of you. Hold this position.

④ Return your foot to its original position, and while inhaling again from the soles of your feet, raise the arms on both sides, drawing an arc in the air with your arms.

⑤ Bring the breath to hyaku-e while placing the back of your hands together over your head, then hold the breath and direct it back down to your tanden.

⑥ Still holding the breath, carve an arc in space with the hands again as you bring them back down to your sides.

⑦ Place the back of your hands on your hips.

⑧ While slowly exhaling, bend the upper body backward. Avoid straining and keep relaxed.

⑨ Come back to the upright position, and do the sokushin breathing again: breathe from the soles of your feet, draw the breath up to the crown of the head, hold it, then bring it down to your tanden.

⑩ Bend the upper body forward as you exhale.

⑪ Place your fingers facing outward, back of your hands against the floor. Release any tension while exhaling.

⑫ Come back to the upright position as you breathe from the soles of your feet.

⑬ Bring your hands, palms facing up, to the chest level as you draw the breath up to the crown of your head. Hold the breath gently there, and then direct it down to your tanden.

⑭ Exhale as you slowly lower your arms to your sides. Repeat with the other foot.

天翔 **Tenshō**

Tenshō is practiced in the spirit of magnificence, such as in the image of a celestial white horse, its wings spread as wide as can be, galloping the heavenly skies.

When bending the body forward, keep the upper body loose and easy, and the wrists turned until the palms of your hands make one full rotation.

Relax and expand the ribs when bending backward from the hips, and breathe out comfortably and smoothly. Avoid straining, and keep the chest open. Besides being effective for improving blood circulation, this exercise is also beneficial for persons afflicted with lower-back pain or sensitive to cold.

① Stand with your feet shoulder-width apart, the entire body relaxed.

② As you do sokushin breathing, stretch your arms out to the sides and bring them up to shoulder level.

③ After directing the energy down to tanden, turn the palms of both hands facing up.

④ Breathe out as you bend forward, turning the palms of your hands at the same time.

⑤ While continuing to breathe out, stretch deeper into the bend, turning your palms further as you lower your upper body.

⑥ Breathe in from the soles of your feet and gradually bring your body upright. Draw the breath up to the crown of your head, then bring it back down to your tanden.

⑦ Next, while breathing out, bend backward, turning your outstretched arms so that the palms of the hands face diagonally down. Bend as far as you can without straining, keeping the chest loose and open.

⑧ Return to the upright position as you breathe in from the soles of the feet; arms are at shoulder level.

⑨

⑩

⑨ Breathe out, lowering arms to your sides.

⑩ Completing the exhale returns you to your original starting position.

Taking a hint from the title, practice this exercise with a bright, gay image in mind. *Rengyō* refers to lotus, perhaps floating on a deep blue-colored pond, displaying full blossoms in all their glory.

Sokushin breathing is guided by both hands. At the point that you have drawn your energy to your tanden, bend one knee while stretching the other. Try to maintain upper body flexibility, and keep palms of hands flat on the floor.

If you direct awareness to the tips of your fingers and feet, it will be easier to retain flexibility and the movements will go more smoothly. *Rengyō* helps to keep the waist trim and the thighs slim.

① Stand with feet double shoulder-width apart, the entire body relaxed.

② As you breathe in from the soles of your feet, bring your arms up in front of you to the level of your chest, as if you were wrapping them around the trunk of a large tree. Slowly lower your hips without tensing your muscles.

③ Direct your awareness to your tanden and exhale, shifting your weight over to the right foot.

④ While breathing out, stretch your left leg, and extend the palms of your hands down, as if you were pressing down on something, and then plant them on the floor. Keep sole of the left foot flat on the floor.

⑤ Breathe in from the soles of the feet, and turn your head to the left as you flex the left foot.

⑥ Continuing to inhale, bring your arms in front of you again.

⑦

⑧

⑦ Gradually return your hips to the position in step 2. Direct your awareness again to your tanden and repeat step 3 to 6 for the other side.

⑧ Bring your arms down as you breathe all the way out; your awareness is on the soles of your feet. After exhalation, return to your original position.

The exercise is practiced with a certain energy movement in mind; the body's energy, originating from the tanden, whirls around and then floats away into a boundless cosmos.

If the physical body is a microcosmos, then the tanden would be the sun. Feel the presence and warmth of this sun with the palms of the hands, and, imagining the grand cosmos, gracefully make a circle with your head. The head and shoulders are completely relaxed.

Muhen, when done alone, is practiced accompanied by sokushin breathing. If practiced at the same time with another Nishino Breathing Method exercise, it is done with normal breathing.

① Relax the entire body, feet placed shoulder-width apart. Place both hands over your tanden.

② Breathe in and toss your head to the upper right.

③ Bring your head around to the front as you breathe out.

④ Continue breathing out, making sure that you have not raised or tensed your shoulders.

⑤ In a smooth movement, continue the head's circular movement over the left shoulder and back.

⑥ Keep your consciousness quietly focused on the tanden.

⑦ Calmly continue rolling your head over past the right shoulder.

⑧ Bring your head to the front again.

⑨ When you face the front, complete your exhale.

⑩ On the inhale, toss your head to the upper left.

⑪ Continue as for the right side. Repeat this set several times.

⑫ Return facing the front, keeping awareness on your tanden.

CHAPTER 6

The Meaning of Contemporary Breathing Ascetics

The Human Body is a Small Universe

Human beings are a microcosm of the universe; their bodies function as a unified entity, comprised of many sub-systems that are all coordinated to operate the whole. On another level, the human organism is incomplete; it grows . . here a bit, there a bit . . . striving insatiably for completion and improvement.

To feel fulfillment, that is, physical and emotional realization, it is necessary to be in "partnership" with the greater cosmos. Maintaining the best possible balance of all body parts is necessary.

To cultivate a high-level body of this type, China, India and Japan since antiquity have practiced austerities. Developing superior intelligence, too, was an important goal of asceticism. This is altogether natural when one considers the inseparability of the mind and the body.

Looking back into the past, the mind-body problem has been a persistent one. While it seems inconceivable now to separate the mind from the body, in the manner that some philosophers, scientists, and artists have argued in history, we still carry a dubious legacy of those debates. In spite of the mountain of knowledge we sit on, the concept of engaging the human body holistically—as a unified cerebral and physical organism—sometimes seems as much a challenge today as ever before.

Too many people today seem to lose their original harmonious mind-body balance. Of those who have manifested some wonderful life achievements, I believe they undoubtedly possessed highly-tuned intelligent bodies— at least at the time.

To elevate the level of the body is absolutely essential

to displaying one's abilities and forging ahead with one's life. The problem, of course, is that the ordinary person cannot pull away from his or her work and, like a member of a religious or spiritual order, enter an austerity regimen.

There is the time, location, and money issue; returning to nature and withdrawing from the entanglements of society for a period of time is a challenge for most of us. Neither can one hope to hone one's physical body by mentally-manipulative short-term programs often watered-down for mass consumption. Not in the true sense of elevating the physical body, anyway.

This is where the NBM comes in. Its objective is to establish in the shortest time possible a physical intelligence that fully manifests the body's potential, with a strong center and macrocosmic sense of existence.

A Contemporary Form of Austerities

The NBM is a practical curriculum that weaves together sokushin breathing, a precise methodology, with kanyō and sennen, to create the ideal physical condition known as chūyū. Now I'd like to introduce another important component of the curriculum: the *jūsoku* (generating-energy) method, a contemporary form of "austerities" that enables you to immediately gain a sense of your energy body.

First, a brief summary of the six stages of energy generation. The jūsoku method begins with *ichigen-jūsoku* (single-source generator), which is simply a process of affirming, or "bringing to awareness," if you like, the tanden as a reservoir of energy in the body.

Ordinarily, the *ichigen* of a person who tends to be governed by mental processes is the brain. In the Nishino School, however, the brain-as-the-controller paradigm is turned upside down, and the tanden is taken as the body's initiating force.

Nigen-jūsoku ("two-source generator") affirms the body's two reservoirs of energy, the tanden and the crown, which funnels energy between the heavens and the earth.

Sangen-jūsoku ("three-source generator") affirms the extension of energy outward from the body's three energy reservoirs, the tanden and both hands.

Yongen-jūsoku ("four-source generator") affirms the energy reservoirs of the two hands and two legs and the relationship between the self and the cosmos.

Next, *tagen-jūsoku* ("multi-source generator") encapsulates the other sources of energy generation at a much higher level and brings to awareness the body's countless parts. Each of these parts becomes an energy-generator, possessing the same quality of energy as the original force, at once generating and receiving input from the universe and generating energy in a constant flow.

When one becomes comfortable with tagen-jūsoku, no matter what the circumstances and no matter what the body may be engaged in, a sublime chūyū state is easily entered, and one can distribute ki as one wishes throughout the body.

In the context of ballet, it might mean "going beyond the level of technique, movement becomes art"—in other words, when one moves, there is beauty. In the context of aikido, it means "a brush or strike transcends technique." That is, the body will have attained these high levels of physicality.

The final stage after tagen-jūsoku lies *mugen-jūsoku* (infinite-source generator), which essentially goes beyond "generating" to a state of being where the entire body is a vibrating field of energy.

If one can apply ichigen-jūsoku, then moving from nigen to sangen, yongen, tagen, and mugen, one will ultimately be able to impact the body on a cellular level.

Because the words "gen" (of ichi*gen*, ni*gen*, etc.) and "jūsoku" are very important words, together with "sokushin" ("heart of the foot") and "chūyū" in the NBM vocabulary, let me digress briefly in explaining their roots.

The character "gen" has the meaning "source" in English, but a Japanese-language dictionary reveals a startling 20-plus meanings for this single broadly defined word. Among the major ones are "life force" and "beneficent mother nature"—definitions that fit the original concepts incorporated into the NBM of receiving life-affirming strength and growth toward human fulfillment. Let's look at some others. "Foremost," "head," "master," "great," "good," "beauty," "above," "heaven," "people," and "main." As you can see, it seemed to me that no character was as suitable as "gen" in conveying the image of the human body.

元
gen

For its part, the character for "jūsoku" means "to be satiated." The juxtaposition of the character "soku" (also read as foot) in the compound "jūsoku," since it is also the first part of the compound for "sokushin" ("heart of the foot"), was a happy and perhaps meaningful coincidence. Why the character for foot also means satiety is unknown. I have my own ideas, based on the simple premise that since the legs are in a lower position on the body and support it, true satiety encompasses feelings of satisfaction all the way down to the feet.

充足
jū soku

In the words of the ancient Chinese philosopher Lao-tze, "To know satiety is to avoid humiliation." "A satisfied person," that is, "whole body satisfaction," will be composed no matter what happens.

A chūyū body that knows satiety is the very one that will achieve a high level through the NBM.

Knowing Internal Magma Through Energy Generation

Now, let's look at how the exercises are done.

Ichigen-jūsoku: Stand with feet shoulder-width apart, body relaxed, and place both hands together over your tanden (lower abdomen). This can be done in the sitting position if you wish. Become conscious of your tanden as the generator of your body's energy. Think of this single storehouse as holding the magma beneath the earth's crust—this molten material overflowing with an unknown quantity of energy. Being subtly conscious, with your entire body, of this magma-like life essence bubbling forth from deep inside, send your breath-nourished ki to this source.

At this stage, be careful not to concentrate your consciousness on the abdomen. As soon as one thinks about the center or a central point, the body becomes rigid and other parts are forgotten. Since a part is the whole and the whole is a part, "concentration" is to be avoided.

Again, we can look to the character of "gen" to help us in conducting ichigen-jūsoku. Besides meaning the "source," "gen" also refers to "creation." Thus, it is both "the very part of something" and "the beginning of something." Being conscious of this source enables us to perceive it as the creative storehouse of the body, which is at the same time a part of the greater universe.

In this way, the ichigen or tanden will be filled with

energy. While relaxing your entire body and expelling the breath, it can be beneficial to gently incorporate sokushin breathing.

Nigen-jūsoku is done in the same way as ichigen-jūsoku while standing. Nigen refers to the tanden and the crown of the head (hyaku-e). After doing the ichigen exercise fully, focus on the tanden and hold the palms of your hands directly over the top of your head. In doing so, completely release the tension in your arms and shoulders and hold your spine straight but relaxed.

The hands are high-level sensors having an intelligence that greatly surpasses antenna; they pick up all kinds of stimuli. Located at the body's extremities, they also enable energy to freely enter and leave the body. With the help of the hands, palms facing down, atmospheric pressure is captured and transmitted as celestial

The hands are intelligent sensors, capturing and transmitting celestial energy to the crown of the head.

energy to the crown of the head. This "opens" the crown and the tanden, two sources of energy generation in the body. The main function of nigen-jūsoku is the smooth flow of celestial energy from the top of the head.

The trick is to practice "opening" the top of the head by bringing your awareness to it. As your entire body comes into a chūyū state, the top of your head will naturally become more receptive to energy flow.

Fundamentals of Three-Source and Four-Source Energy Generation

The three-source generator (sangen-jūsoku) is the foundation of the jūsoku method. It involves the tanden and both hands. It can be done either standing or sitting with the legs folded underneath (you can also sit with the legs crossed comfortably in front of you if this is difficult). The entire body is relaxed, the spinal column is straight, and awareness is brought to the tanden and both hands.

Tapping into these three reservoirs of energy elevates the entire body, creating an expansion and flow—like a radiation or vibration of an "undefinable something" outward.

If we take the view that our hands are our second brain, when both hands are fully suffused with energy, one can calmly and sweepingly comprehend things. In a state of sangen-jūsoku the body is very tranquil, and a strong atmosphere pervades of deep profoundness.

The yongen-jūsoku involves standing with the legs shoulder-width apart, body relaxed and loose. The four sources refer to both hands and feet, the second brain and second heart respectively. As awareness is brought to both hands and feet, the other parts of the body are left "empty."

An Unlimited World Through Multi-Source Energy Generation

Generating energy from multiple sources is the next advanced stage after you have mastered the one-source and two-source generation (the two basic exercises) and is able to apply three-source and four-source generation as well.

"Multi" in this context refers to an infinite number of points all over the body. If you consider all the body's cells, it may be easier to understand. These cells are tiny generator sites; the entire body is suffused with energy, maximizing its free flow throughout the body.

When these sites are opened to generate energy, ki emanates like an aura from all over the body and the skill to control it will gradually become apparent. As ki fills the body, you will acquire more latitude, with the pleasing result that causing or wishing harm on yourself or others will become a thing of the past. Since others become enveloped in your ki, naturally you will succumb to fewer injuries. You will find yourself in fewer uncomfortable— or dangerous—situations, and instead feel happier and experience stronger self-esteem.

In yongen-jūsoku (four-source generator) you can see inside your own body. In tagen-jūsoku (multi-source generator) you do not simply conceive of your existence but can actually grasp it physically—enabling you to see beyond the self. While your immediate surroundings may seem clear enough, to take in the reality of it is difficult.

That's where physical intelligence, or "body perception," comes in.

If the body is well honed, one will understand the early 4th century Chinese military strategist Sun-tzu when he said, "Win without a fight." First of all, contentious situations are almost entirely avoided. When they cannot be avoided, they are simply dissolved. The strength involved is "zero strength," that is, it comes by overwhelming the opponent and absorbing his or her aggression. It is abiding the storm and becoming as calm as a great sea. In this lies the ultimate strength of life.

The seventh century Hindu algebraist Brahmagupta postulated that zero multiplied by any factor always has a value of zero. Therefore, "zero" has an unlimited capacity no matter what it encompasses. No matter what value zero is added to or subtracted from, that value remains the same. ($a + 0 = a$, $a - 0 = a$). Zero, then, opposes nothing, tries to change nothing, and is unlimited in its compatibility. The strength of ki energy is similar to the value of zero; it has absolute flexibility.

Cultivating this "zero-strength" of life is the function of efficient breathing. And efficient breathing results in unlimited control over chūyū and jūsoku.

呼気
ko ki

+

吸気
kyū ki

‖

呼吸
(zero or ideal
respiration)

Koki (out-breath or yang/plus) + kyūki (in-breath or yin/minus) = zero. Efficient breathing is the key that opens the door to the secrets of zero. And, tagen-jūsoku opens the door to the highest stage, of infinite energy generation.

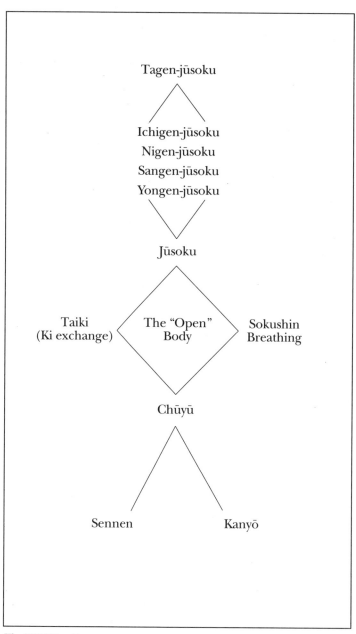

The NBM Paradigm

Ki Fosters Our Freedom

Time is a product of our minds, formed by our sensibility or perception. But for our physical being, direct sensory cognition here and now is everything. I return to the idea of acquiring freedom beyond temporal, physical limitations by breathing deeply and feeling the air passing as a medium between us and the outside world (Chapter 1). Freedom from time, or put another way, experiencing the eternal moment, can be a common experience by the power of the breath.

Using the NBM, you can begin to measure time in your unique physical way. The NBM is a technique that more than anything else places importance on one's fundamental sense of well-being, and there is no sense of well-being so profound as having freedom within one's own body. This includes the abilities to feel awe and experience miracles large and small *every single day of our lives.* Albert Einstein said that those who cannot experience wonder are as good as dead. Our path to such freedom is by developing intelligent bodies.

Strength is Necessary for Survival

The NBM ensures a slim, tenacious body, a rush of latent powers, and the flowering of one's destiny.

Thus far I've discussed the Nishino Breathing Method in general terms, but now let me explain a bit about what "strength" means in the context of creating a "slim, tenacious body."

To refer to strength straightforwardly at the basic animal level, it pertains to animal aggression or the instinctive struggle for existence.

Austrian zoologist and Nobel laureate Konrad Lorenz' thesis on animal aggression is of interest here. According to his theory, animals ensure their existence through aggression (i.e., their killer instinct) and when this instinct weakens, they become extinct.

Strength in its fundamental form as manifested in aggression is the life-origin of animals and human beings alike. Human beings, too, must go on living by becoming strong.

Tales about Japanese samurai warriors (read avidly by their modern-day counterparts, the Japanese businessman) do not highlight the techniques required to win battles or the mental fortitude befitting the strong but the hidden physical powers that are summoned forth when needed. In Europe, too, aggressive strength was a desirable physical quality encompassed within the framework of the knight's chivalry. This very code aimed toward establishing a virtuous, honorable order for aggression. While some adhered only nominally to this code, it was nevertheless an attempt to elevate—or cloak—an innate, animalistic force in a cultured, humanistic form.

Knights later were succeeded by gentlemen, by nonmilitary men of letters and other achievements. For many people the word "gentleman" probably suggests the meaning "genteel" (having a privileged upbringing by being born to wealth), but the English poet Chaucer maintained that anyone who was sincere, benevolent, free, and brave was a gentleman. Here, too, we see a definite physical strength. That is, at any given moment no matter what conditions the gentleman may encounter, he does not lose composure. He can cope with anything. We seek such physical tenacity even now, as human beings have done everywhere through the ages.

A Graceful Life is the Platform to Progress

"Tenacity," though, as I use it in this book has no reference whatsoever to fighting or conflict. Rather, it refers to the life-force strength, which is supported by the physical organism. For example, the virtues of a calm forbearance in overcoming a difficult situation is part of it.

Large-scale projects cannot be carried out on the basis of good luck alone. Without fail, some trying moments will also come along. When they do, one must conserve one's strength, waste no effort, and wait for the tide to turn. This forbearance is a different matter from simply suppressing one's selfish desires and bearing with it. Rather, it means going beyond oneself, and beyond one's surroundings, and storing up sufficient life-energy to achieve a greater self.

The good thing about forbearance is that it provides flexibility for life that conceals, so to speak, the next big step. To achieve this forbearance, however requires a kind of tensile strength. The strength that enables athletes to overcome slumps is this kind of resilient life tenacity. The best athletes invariably experience slumps, but they must be able to overcome them.

This resilient strength and tenacity is evident in women and especially mothers. A mother provides all manner of tangibles and intangibles to her child, and carries the responsibility to enable it to go on living. In her life-force strength, a mother possesses something that can't be measured. Could it be this that enables women in general to live longer than men during times of famine?

During the Edo period in Japan (1615–1868), cultural activities of all sorts flourished. What made it possible was the briskly developing commerce, and, it is said, the merchants' wives who supported this commercial growth. Merchants of this era at times employed a few dozen apprentices. With the broad-mindedness characteristic of women, these wives meticulously looked after each apprentice's individual needs. Not only that, they maintained close ties with their contractors, entertained customers, and in general took charge and succeeded in building up a reputable business. This indeed showed tremendous tenacity.

Nor of course is this strength on the part of women limited to the wives of Edo merchants alone. Housewives happily maintaining homes in general have this quality of life power. Mothers' life energy circulates among family members like ki and the breath in the body, relieving fatigue and invigorating everyone. "Tenacity" is a resilient life energy, existing in supporting all manner of life's offerings.

True Strength is an Eternal Theme of the Human Body

I have always placed my faith in life and in the overall view that holds life as good. I can see, however, how people might get caught up in the survival struggle and find no joy in the pursuit of it.

Often people experience so much pain and struggle

in life that it represents "evil" and/or "nihilism." Undoubtedly life contains elements of both. But the former statement does not follow from the latter. Life encompasses both . . . and not only that, it also includes "death."

"Death" cannot encompass "life." And of course "evil" and "nihilism" cannot encompass "life." In seeking a higher level of "life," we must strive to elevate our level of tolerance and strength, a strength not on the level of Lorenz' animal aggression but as sufficient life force that shapes human culture and civilization, and one that can overcome "evil," "nihilism," and "death."

In establishing the self, in living a culturally- and intellectually-rich life, and in living a life based on love and goodness, strength is indispensable. The NBM seeks to nourish this kind of strength.

Physical Intelligence Makes Escape from Weakness Possible

A world where people live open to the energy flow within the cosmos is clearly a peaceful world.

On a visit to Hawaii to make a video on breathing some years ago, I spotted a book prominently displayed on a shelf in a bookstore: *Out of Weakness*. On the cover was an illustration of two horsemen that attracted me, but what really surprised me was its title—so akin to what I'm feeling every day.

The subtitle was "Healing the Wounds That Drive Us to War." The author, Andrew Schmookler, is a Harvard University professor in psychology. To sum up the gist of his writings, human beings do not become warlike through power. Rather, it is weakness that incites people to fight. Schmookler maintains that it is not out of fear of combat with an enemy but rather to flee from the demon residing in one's own sense of weakness that drives men to wage war.

Schmookler refers to two meanings in his use of "out of weakness." One is "from" weakness of a past filled with conflicts, and the other is "beyond" weakness to overcome difficult situations in the present.

To overcome struggle, obviously it is necessary to conquer weakness. This book seemed to support my daily thoughts that having a strong life force is the best way to conquer weakness. When I think about strength, I mean the survival-instinct strength on a biological level— together with the physical intelligence that is nurtured from effective breathing.

Out of Weakness is about an America that once again tends toward a "strong America" and "strong people." This is indeed proof of America's wholesomeness. America, in always retaining a sense of its people ("cells") and its nation ("body"), may be said to be the most wholesome country of all.

Out of Weakness is also very interesting in that as a means of conquering weakness it focuses on the body at the cellular level and the quantum level. The body is seen as a small universe existing in harmony with the universe. An unfortunate fact, however, is that it does not indicate a concrete solution that might make it possible to rid oneself of weakness.

Even if one intellectually comprehends the thesis posited by Schmookler, that itself will not rid one of weakness. I believe only by conquering weakness with the body can one become strong. This book, in fact, is an example of how ineffectual intellectual solutions are in bringing about fundamental change. The major problem in the 21st century will be the problem of peace—and this problem is indispensably linked to human weakness.

We might go as far as to say that so long as people do not overcome mental or psychological weakness at the cellular level, conflict will never disappear from the face of the earth. In taking this to heart, the new millennium will clearly emerge not as one of cerebral intelligence but of physical intelligence.

A Parting Word

楽
RAKU=happy

The NBM has a pose called "raku" that involves standing with both arms extended and hands lightly flexed at the wrists. This is the position you see on the cover of this book. It clearly reflects a fundamental NBM concept.

It often happens, however, that by extending the arms to the side, the muscles of the shoulders and chest tense. Consciousness also rises to the chest, resulting in a state of imbalance due to a high center of gravity.

When you get the drift of sokushin breathing, however, and your body enters a state of chūyū, you'll understand why this position feels most pleasant. Plant your feet firmly in the ground and look up into the heavens and in your heart you'll feel keenly your tranquil, open self.

With arms fully extended, this position is the source of the sense of flowing in the NBM. I personally think it's a lot of fun. I believe when one experiences fun or pleasure, it is the ultimate state of a harmonious mind and body.

"Liking is superior to knowing. And enjoying is best."
These words are from Confucius, the sixth-century B.C.
Chinese philosopher, according to the *Analects of Confucius.* Cognitive knowledge can't compete with true interest and curiosity. And interest and curiosity cannot hold a
candle to true enjoyment. Even Sakyamuni (Buddha), in
the end, reached a state of satiety—of raku.

The fact that this pleasure is none other than the pleasure obtained from extending one's arms is something I experienced in my body when I created the raku position. In NBM, experiencing this is the most important thing of all. It is the pleasure of living in the great universe, and that pleasure is the motive power of one's own individual "biospark," or the spark of life.

The NBM, through sokushin breathing, chūyū, jūsoku energy generation, and taiki, can enable you to manifest innate powers, along with that joie de vivre, at will. It redirects the body, making possible the pleasure of working out one's destiny.